*A History of the*

# CENTRAL MARINE
# ENGINE WORKS

## 1884 – 1961

Peter L. Hogg, FICS

*Published by*
Hartlepool Borough Council
1995

# Dedication

*This book is dedicated to the past citizens of this town who created the Central Marine Engine Works, and to those who carried on the fine engineering traditions of that establishment until its closure. The C.M.E.W. cantilever crane was a notable landmark in this town for almost 50 years, and thanks are due to Hartlepool Borough Council for publishing this part of the town's history.*

**ISBN 0 9501306 7 2**

*Printed by:*
Atkinson Print, 11 Lower Church Street, Hartlepool, Cleveland TS24 7DJ
Telephone: (01429) 267849   Fax: (01429) 865416

# *Foreword*

by

## Sir William Gray, Baronet

*(great-great-grandson of the founder)*

This story of the achievements of the Central Marine Engine Works is long overdue as all too quickly time dims the memory of the once familiar. In the world of shipping, where the British were once pre-eminent, the workforce of the Hartlepools, especially those of the Central Marine Engine Works, were held in high regard for their engineering skills and enterprise. However, the ever increasing pace of change of the modern era has now left behind a once flourishing community.

Very often records of industrial history are complex and dry. However, this record of the Central Marine Engine Works enlightens with its descriptions of the several technologies employed. The events that formed, shaped and finally laid the business to rest are all described in careful detail. Dedicated research has also resurrected many of the characters behind the success of the business, drawing on the recollections of those who knew the works at first hand. This book serves as a fitting tribute to all their endeavours.

William Gray.
Eggleston Hall, Barnard Castle                    January 1995.

# Contents

# CENTRAL MARINE ENGINE WORKS, HARTLEPOOL.

## THE CREATION OF THE WORKS.

THIS book is an attempt to fill one of the many gaps caused by the comparative neglect by historians of the 19th century marine engine makers - neglect compared with the attention paid to the shipbuilders. Thanks to some few records preserved in Hartlepool Maritime Museum and to the scouring of Lloyd's Registers by some devoted helpers, it has been possible to build up what it is hoped is a not far from complete list of the output of the works.

About 1882, or perhaps earlier (see page 2) William Gray decided to set up his own engine works to supplement his shipbuilding activities. He was a very successful shipbuilder, having started with a drapery business in 'Old' Hartlepool, and then (as so many local people did) bought 64th shares in ships. Most of the ships in which he had money must have done well and given a good return on the 64ths he held, as he quite soon was building a sizeable sailing vessel ("Blanche") in John Punshon Denton's Middleton yard as a joint venture with the builder.

William Gray (1823-1898: Knighted 1890)
*(Courtesy of Hartlepool Museums Service)*

There are numerous records of the rise of the William Gray business, so it seems unnecessary to record here the early history of the enterprise, which had, by the end of 1882, already built more than 170 ships (first as Denton, Gray & Co. and then as William Gray & Co.) Denton himself had launched 54 ships before William Gray joined him.

However, as in 1882 there were many engine-builders in the Tees, the Wear and the Tyne, and a very successful one in Hartlepool in the shape of Thomas Richardson & Sons, with over 30 years experience of marine engine production, it was a bold step to create his own establishment. Perhaps he wanted for his own company the engine profit, or perhaps he felt that engine-builders might hold him to ransom.

The choice of engine suppliers for locally built ships in the years 1882 to 1891 is shown in Table 1 below:-

| Table 1. | | ENGINE | SALES | | | | |
|---|---|---|---|---|---|---|---|
| THOS. RICHARDSON | | | | CENTRAL MARINE | | | |
| YEAR | GRAY NEWBD. | OTHER YARDS | TOTAL | GRAY'S LAUNCH | GRAY NEWBD. | OTHER YARDS | TOTAL |
| 1882 | 5 | 26 | 31 | 23 | 0 | 0 | 0 |
| 1883 | 4 | 36 | 40 | 20 | 0 | 0 | 0 |
| 1884 | 4 | 17 | 21 | 11 | 0 | 0 | 0 |
| 1885 | 0 | 15 | 15 | 12 | 4 | 0 | 4 |
| 1886 | 0 | 13 | 13 | 8 | 6 | 1 | 7 |
| 1887 | 1 | 16 | 17 | 10 | 8 | 3 | 11 |
| 1888 | 0 | 22 | 22 | 20 | 10 | 2 | 12 |
| 1889 | 0 | 34 | 34 | 30 | 28 | 2 | 30 |
| 1890 | 0 | 22 | 22 | 27 | 25 | 3 | 28 |
| 1891 | 0 | 28 | 28 | 24 | 23 | 1 | 24 |

Having decided to commit the necessary capital to the venture, William Gray then engaged a young man of 30 to head the enterprise. This was Thomas Mudd (born Kirby Fleetham 1852), a very clever engineer who had started his career at Darlington Forge and had been ten years with Thomas Richardsons of Hartlepool. Mudd was to design the entire works and this he did in a thoroughly practical way, basing his lay-out on the flow of work throughout the various stages of manufacture. All the stages were catered for - foundry, forge, machine shops, boiler shops, auxiliaries, etc. The chosen site was a large vacant area on the north side of the Basin (with a 57' 6" lock at each end) which had been created a few years earlier by the North Eastern Railway in linking the Old Harbour at Hartlepool with the West Hartlepool dock system. Part of the large former Slake area of tidal mudflats was used in this creation of Union Dock, Central Dock and the North Basin, which began in 1875 and was completed in 1880. Gray leased the engine works site from the N.E.R., complete with 700 foot long quay, and the N.E.R. had built a 600 foot drydock in the adjacent Central Dock. It has been suggested that the availability of this 200-acre site with quay frontage may have resulted from some prior arrangement between Gray and the N.E.R. William Gray was, after all, a local director of the Railway Company. If there is any value in that suggestion, it must surely point to a much earlier date for William Gray's ideas about an engine works.

The plans of Thomas Mudd's original concept have survived - probably because in December 1886 he gave a very full paper on the subject to the North East Coast Institution of Engineers and Shipbuilders, and his paper was published in their Transactions for 1886-7.

It was rare for an engineer to have the opportunity to start from scratch with a quite major engine works: so many older establishments had grown from small beginnings, often on rather cramped sites, with all the disadvantages such growth entails. For Thomas Mudd to have this opportunity at age 30 must have been the realisation of the dream of many engineers. The nature of the site and the amount of land available (some ten acres) imposed some restrictions on the chosen lay-out, but his design found reasonable favour with many eminent local engineers who heard his paper read. Rail access to (and into) the works was, of course, provided. The main shops were lit by fifty large electric arc lamps, each of 2000 candle-power; general illumination was by gas. Mudd's paper is very detailed, and was printed complete with comments made by many fellow engineers in his audience during the discussion which followed.

The quay, to be used for engine installation, was equipped with a small hydraulic crane and an hydraulic powered sheer-legs of 80 tons capacity, which sufficed from 1885 to 1914, when it was replaced with a 100-ton cantilever crane by Cowans & Sheldon, Carlisle - a landmark in the town until its eventual demolition after the closure of William Gray's establishment.

Much of 1883 and all of 1884 was used in the creation of the works and installation of the machinery. The first section set up was the loam foundry, which was put to immediate use to cast the iron columns for the roof supports and the overhead crane tracks, as well as other components needed for the construction of the buildings.

In the forge one of the hammers (a 5 tonner) was acquired second-hand from the Thames Iron Co. at Greenwich; it had been used in making some parts of Brunel's 'Great Eastern' in 1858, and must have been solidly made, as it continued in use for many years, and the hammer's base anvil was so large and heavy that it was left in situ when the works closed in 1962.

# EARLY OUTPUT.

The first marine engine sold was a triple expansion, installed in the local shipowner George Pyman's "Enfield" in 1885, and most of the earlier production was of triples, though a few two-cylinder compound engines were produced in the first years.

The works had a tradition of making as much as possible of its own equipment - later this was exemplified when, in 1904, they built two triple expansion engines for electrical power generation for the shops. These engines were included in the engine list (216 & 218) and were named 'Bradgate' and 'Tunstall' respectively, after the homes of George Henry Baines, who was the first Managing Director of the Central Marine Engine Works, and of William Cresswell Gray, his brother-in-law, who was now at the head of the William Gray organisation, after the death of William Gray, Senior.

This first Tunstall Manor was demolished after about 30 years, and George Baines' home "Bradgate" was renamed "Westlands" when it passed into other hands after the death of George Baines in 1913. The latter house still exists in 1995, somewhat altered by successive owners.

The years 1884 to 1887 were reported as somewhat depressed years for the shipbuilding industry, so William Gray started his Central Marine Engine Works at an unfortunate time. Some shipowners even turned once more to sail, and in the years 1884 and 1885 Gray built seven sailing ships. Thomas Richardson, who had for so long been the sole marine engine builder in The Hartlepools must have been somewhat dismayed to see the start of a competitor, particularly one who enticed away one of his bright young engineers. In fact, in the years immediately prior to the start of Central Marine there had not been a large number of orders coming Richardsons' way in respect of Gray-built ships, as evidenced in Table I. Orders had gone to several different works, as one can see from B. G. Spaldin's "Shipbuilders of The Hartlepools".

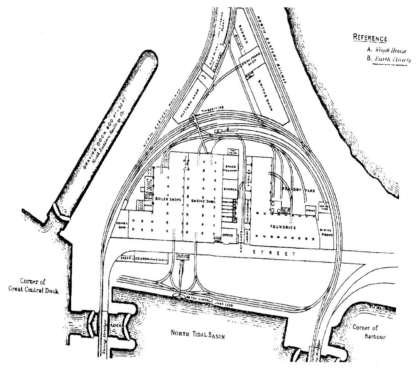

Works of the Central Marine Engineering Company, Hartlepool.

Two N.E.R. drydocks (in Central Dock) are shown in one small plan with Mudd's paper, but only one was ever built. This was retained by the N. E. Railway as a 'common user' or public graving dock, and Grays built their Central shipyard next to it, in 1887, on land leased from the North Eastern Railway, which owned the entire dock system (Hartlepool & West Hartlepool) and the dock estate. That shipyard (Gray's third in West Hartlepool) was considered necessary in order to build larger ships than was possible in the other two, those in the Jackson and Swainson Docks.

George H. Baines, born Leicester in 1842, and married to William Gray's daughter (Dorothy Wilson Gray), had a successful wholesale ironmongery business in Leicester, and just why he left that and came to work with his father-in-law, accepting an appointment as Managing Director of CMEW, has never been explained, so far as the Author is aware. He was without doubt a success in that post, and became fully integrated into the life of the town. He and Thomas Mudd seemed able to work effectively together. Baines made his home first at "Bradgate" (a Leicester reference) in Victoria Road, but soon built a new and larger home off Park Avenue, near his brother-in-law's Tunstall Manor, giving the new house the same name. Mrs. Baines died in 1905.

# DEATHS OF WILLIAM GRAY & THOMAS MUDD.

Thomas Mudd was General Manager until his untimely death at 46 during his third term of office as Mayor of (Old) Hartlepool, in May of 1898; he died at his home ("Greencliffe", Cliff Terrace, on the Headland), and after the funeral service at St. Hilda's Church his body went by rail to Manchester Crematorium, accompanied by both the St. Hilda's curates: cremation was very unusual in those days, and the Church Burial Register entry goes into some detail on the arrangements.

That year also witnessed the death of William Gray, founding father of the enterprise, who was succeeded by his elder son, William Cresswell Gray. Matthew, younger son of the first William Gray, who had been active in the business and in other industrial spheres as well, had died two years earlier, in 1896. St. Oswald's Church, Brougham Terrace, is his widow's memorial to Matthew Gray.

Mudd's successor as General Manager at Central Marine was William Cameron Borrowman, whose tenure of office was from 1898 to his retirement in 1907. He lived at 'Newstead House' in lower Grange Road, West Hartlepool. No Company press release on his appointment (or his departure) has been found, but his obituary in "The Engineer" of 1911 describes him as a gifted Scottish engineer, who had been a Whitworth Scholar. From the same source we learn that he came to Central Marine from a Manager's position at Barclay Curle of Glasgow, and that he was born in Auchtermuchty, Forfarshire.

Thomas Mudd

G. H. Baines was in reality, perhaps, 'Financial Manager', while at the outset Thomas Mudd was General Manager AND Works Manager: Mudd filled this dual role for the first two years of full operation, but before very long William Gray had insisted that the post of Works Manager should be separated and a new appointment made. Archibald M. Henderson of Harland & Wolff was therefore engaged in 1887 as the first Works Manager. He took a property in Greatham Terrace (No. 3), in what was then Clarence Road (now Lancaster Road), and Ossie Lumsden, a later holder of the same position, related that Henderson made a stately arrival at work each day on board a CMEW rail locomotive, which picked him up each morning at the Greenland crossing near his home. One assumes that his return home would be in the same unusual way.  Later Archie Henderson moved to "Bennochy", Elm Grove, West Hartlepool.  During the entire life of the works there were only three Works Managers - Archie Henderson,  Marmont Warren and J. O. Lumsden.  The same remarkable record probably also applies to the uniformed gatemen, of whom the last two were Parker (about 1906 to 1933) and V. Woods ('Woodsie') who reigned from 1933 to 1959.  Both are remembered with some affection by lads who worked under them as Gatehouse boys while awaiting their chance to become indentured.

There can be no doubt that Thomas Mudd was a bold and inventive engineer: he has a long series of patents against his name (at least 36 in the 12 years from 1885, for instance), and some of these will fall within the ambit of this book.  As early as 1886 (the second year of production), when trade was improving and orders coming in to the shipyard, Mudd was contracting to supply two sets of triple-expansion engines of guaranteed performance for 4000 ton DWT ships to be built by Grays for the Great Western S.S. Co. of Bristol.  These engines (Nos. 12 & 13) were of 1300 IHP, to give the ships a service speed of 9.5 knots fully laden, with enough power to attain 10.5 knots case need.  Consumption at service speed was guaranteed not to exceed 18 tons Best Welsh coal per day.

Engines 5, 6 and 7 from the Works were 2-cylinder compound engines for three small 'flatiron colliers'; two of 688 Gross Tons and one of 886 Gross Tons, all for F. Green of London, built by Grays at a total cost of £11,000 each  complete.  Although the two-cylinder compound engine was 'old technology' by that date, since the triple expansion engine had been widely adopted by then, for coasting vessels there was still a demand for

Loam Foundry 1886 *(Courtesy of Hartlepool Museums Service)*

them. The cost was less than for a triple, and the smaller engine room (and lower weight) meant more cargo capacity, even though the fuel consumption was greater. The fuel economy of the triple made that type desirable in vessels making longer voyages and having to bunker with coals much more expensive than in the U.K. Two of these colliers with 2-cylinder engines ("Stepney" and "Wapping") were reported on in "Engineering" of 17th September 1886: Mudd's inventiveness had even invaded these engines - they were fitted with Mudd's "patent dynamic valve gear", described elsewhere as piston valves.

In consequence of CMEW's growing reputation for building an economical (and durable) triple expansion engine it was almost standard to have CMEW engines specified for Gray-built ships from 1888 onwards. Not only that, but they quickly obtained a modest share of the business of modernising the engines of older vessels which had been built from about 1870 with two-cylinder compound engines - triple expansion machinery had not really come into its own until 1883. An early and unusual quadruple expansion engine (on only two cranks - engine No. 19) was contrived for the modernising in 1887 of the two-cylinder compound engine in the "Suez", which had been built in 1876, but there is no sign of the works having been asked to repeat that particular conversion, even though a 34% saving in fuel consumption was claimed. In that same year they tripled the "Jenny Otto" (built 1877). The following year (1888) they took in hand the "Walmer Castle" of 1872, and the specialist press reported very favourably on the fact that after the engine had been tripled and the ship re-boilered the length of the engine and boiler space was 28 feet less than that originally installed: this was engine No. 42. The major share of tripling older compound engines in Hartlepool, however, went to Thomas Richardsons on the other side of the North Basin. It was 1890 before Central Marine are recorded as re-engining another older vessel - this was engine No. 78, a triple put in the German "Tetartos", built in 1883, to replace a 2-cylinder compound: the ship's coal usage fell from 23 tons per day to 14 tons. These modernisation operations sometimes consisted of installing a new engine, but in many cases parts of the old engine were retained and a two cylinder compound would have an additional cylinder added: there were several ways of improving these older engines, some of which showed great ingenuity.

Mudd took out a patent in 1888 (No. 12792) on a quadruple expansion engine, which appears to have been very like that of William Allan of Scotia Works, Sunderland: it certainly had the first (HP) cylinder carried above the normal bank of three cylinders, but this layout from all works suffered mechanical troubles, and was soon dropped for the 'in-line' type of engine - a style which became standard for the later 'Quad' engines from Central Marine. Four expansions of steam required a higher boiler pressure, and Mudd's patent stated:-

"there need be no difficulty in going as far as 225 pounds per square inch with boilers of 11 feet or even 12 feet in diameter". (See page 9)

In 1888 the Gray shipyards won the Blue Riband (for maximum output from a yard) for the third time, launching 20 ships: only eleven of these were CMEW engined; the engines for the other nine came from Blairs of Stockton-on-Tees, who were major engine builders by that time.

By 1889 the demand on the company for forgings, including major work such as stern-frames, was such that a new forge was installed, with the latest hammers and other equipment. The building for this addition was acquired from Antwerp, where it had been

## QUADRUPLE EXPANSION ENGINES.

MR. THOMAS MUDD, CENTRAL MARINE ENGINEERING WORKS, WEST HARTLEPOOL, ENGINEER.

used in an exhibition, and was reputed to have the largest clear span of any in existence, being 500 feet long and 85 feet wide. A long report in the South Durham Herald of 14th December 1889 tells us there were now 10 steam hammers, and other equipment included machines for "slotting, pintle turning, gudgeon boring, boring, shaping and scarfing" plus a multiple drilling machine "containing no less than 28 drills".

More than 1500 people were now employed at Central Marine - 27 sets of machinery (almost 30,000 IHP) had been produced in the year, while the total boiler output was 60: four new machine tools had been installed in the boiler shop. Perhaps of greater interest is the fact that three of the 27 sets of machinery had been "fitted with Mr. Fothergill's Forced Draught". The newspaper report ends with "the reputation for high economy of the engines turned out is growing by leaps and bounds".

The works was capable of what the local press described as "quick engineering": in many cases an engine could be installed at the sheerlegs and the vessel be carrying out steaming trials within 3-5 days of arrival at the fitting out berth. In August of 1890 the "Rangitira", "Halifax City" and "Manchester" followed on the Basin berth one after the other and all were engined "within a few days". These were some of the 30 ships engined that year (total IHP 37,100), into which 61 "high-pressure" boilers were fitted, while 23 other boilers had been sold. Output of castings was 4,100 tons in spite of a ten week strike, and included 100 propellers, "of which 40 are for old steamers to replace their propellers, this speciality at Central Marine coming greatly into favour".

By the end of the 1880's CMEW engines were efficient and economical to a degree which attracted favourable comment in the technical press, and Robert Craig reports on this aspect in his work "Wm. Gray & Co. 1864-1913". Coal consumption was down to 1.39 - 1.41 pounds per indicated horsepower per hour. Gray's "Inchbarra", of 1891, 6220 tons carrying capacity, had sailed at a continuous 10 knots on 20.3 tons of coal per day, carrying 6272 tons. Hers was a triple-expansion engine (No. 109).

The build quality of both ships and engines is illustrated by the fact that the "Norlands" (Grays 353, with engine number 37), built in 1889 was still sailing under Spanish Flag in 1961.

"Norlands" (Gray 353) in 1961 *(Courtesy Hartlepool Museums Service)*

When Grays built the quite small steamer "General Boyd" in 1891 she was fitted with a 2-cylinder compound engine of 217 NHP from Central Marine: it was not common by that date not to take a triple for a normal cargo vessel, though some smaller ships in the coastal trades were the exception at dates even much later than this. In 1892, on the 8th of May the newbuilt s.s. "Manica" (Wm. Gray Yard No. 438) did her sea trials on a Sunday - a most unusual occurrence.

## SOME CONVERSIONS TO TRIPLE.

The Company's press release of December 1893 gave the year's output as 25 sets (36,500 IHP), and the eight year total from start-up as 170 sets (212,000 IHP). Three ships appear in that listing but not in the works engine book. These were "Sweden" of 1869, "Mark Lane" of 1878 and "Albania" of 1883 (Gray-built with a Black, Hawthorn engine) - not new buildings, but ships in for engine conversions. It appears that their original 2-cylinder engines were up-rated at CMEW by fitting two new cylinders of different dimensions, with new boilers, and not given new engines nor converted to triples - possibly because the engine-room dimensions would not take the extra length of a triple-expansion engine. Boiler pressures for these three vessels are given in Lloyd's Register of 1894-5 as 120, 130 and 150 pounds per sq. inch, which seems unusually high for a two-cylinder compound engine. s.s."Sweden" was certainly overdue for new engines and boiler: Lloyd's Register of 1887-8 shows that her approved boiler pressure had been reduced from 32 pounds to 10 pounds for her original George Clark 2-cylinder simple engine (34" & 34" x 28" stroke). The other two ships had been operating on 80 pounds steam pressure. The stroke of all three of these engines remained unchanged after uprating, as did the NHP of each engine. The press reported a similar operation on "Larch" (built Sunderland 1878) in 1894, and also "Gardepee" of 1882 in the same year - a change of cylinder sizes on a 2-cylinder compound, plus new boilers of higher pressure than would be expected for such a two cylinder compound engine: in the case of "Gardepee" this was a surprising 160 pounds. Perhaps the marine engineers of the day were able to juggle with valve settings which enabled them to run compounds economically on high steam pressures, or maybe they ran the boilers at less than their rated pressure: no records exist, it seems, of the normal practice at sea, when engines would run for long periods at one setting. Once again engine numbers appear not to have been allocated, and it is very probable, as G. B. Butler has pointed out to the author, that work of this nature may well have been carried out on other ships and not been picked up in making the list of works output.

## 5-CRANK QUADS & WARRANTIES.

Thomas Mudd was convinced he could better the already good performance of his engines. He had already patented (in 1888) his first version of the quadruple expansion engine, using an extra expansion of steam from better boilers, capable of supplying steam at the higher pressure needed for effective use of the extra stage in the engine. The "Inchbarra" owners (Hamilton, Fraser & Co., Glasgow) built the "Inchmona" at Gray's yard in 1895 as a 5000 tonner. She had the first of Mudd's newest & up-dated patent 5-crank in-line quadruple expansion engines (Engine & Yard No. 512), and Mudd was so confident that he persuaded his directors to agree the following remarkable warranty on the engine's performance:-

> Our expectation is that consumption will be about 1.15 lbs per IHP per hour, and in recognition of your enterprise in ordering this machinery, we only propose that you shall be called upon to pay the sum of £3,000 in case the coal consumption falls as low as 1.1 lbs/IHP/hour, whilst for every 0.1lb that the coal consumption is greater the payment will fall £500, and

proportionately with regard to all intermediate values. That is to say, the payment dependent on results, shown in tabular form, will be as follows:-

| Consumption | Payment |
|---|---|
| Lbs | £ |
| 1.100 or less | 3000 |
| 1.125 | 2875 |
| 1.150 | 2750 |
| and so on to: | |
| 1.6 | 500 |
| 1.7 | nil |

So that in the extremely improbable result of the consumption being as high as 1.7 you will be called upon for no payment whatever. Agreed that the results of the first voyage be neglected - second and third voyages to be basis: purchaser to furnish a reliable chief engineer with William Gray supplying a supernumerary chief engineer who is to give his best services to the management of the machinery, we paying his wages throughout the first, second and third voyages, but you finding him in food. Coal to be good Cardiff or Barry coal to mutual approval".

[Note: No record has been found to indicate what level of payment Owners had to make after the consumption on the 2nd and 3rd voyages had been evaluated.]

Mudd's Patent Five-Crank Marine Engine

"Nassovia" (Gray 623) 1900 *(Courtesy of H. S. Appleyard)*

Other "quads" followed, but this five-crank type of engine (the first of its kind) was not the success which had been hoped for it, and it was not widely adopted. There were several reasons for this - the conservatism of shipowners, the higher initial cost, the complication of the engine, the need for higher boiler pressure and hence better boiler management than for a triple, and the fact that the longer engine reduced the cubic space in the ship available for cargo. Hamilton, Fraser took three more in 1900, and Hamburg shipowner Robt. M. Sloman agreed a quad in his "Nassovia", ordered 1899 and delivered in 1901. These "Inch" vessels had cylinders of 17″, 24″, 34″, 42″ and 42″ with a stroke of 42″ on all five cranks. The boiler pressure was 225 pounds per square inch - considerably higher than the usual 160 lbs for triples at that date. According to Lloyd's Register the "Nassovia" boilers produced 268 pounds per square inch.

By that time the superheating of steam was coming into use, and the forced draught systems of Howden and others had been more widely introduced. These systems increased the efficiency of the standard triple expansion engine, and certainly forced draught allowed more effective use of inferior bunker coals.

In 1891 Mudd took out a patent on a new type of boiler, made from steel produced by the Weardale Iron & Steel Co. This was one of the very many patents he took out during his time at Central Marine - all appear to have been in his own name. Engines and boilers are the usual subjects, but one for which publicity was achieved was his patent sleeving for protecting propeller shafts from corrosion. The results of examination late in 1894 of Mudd-protected tail shafts of three vessels ("Zanzibar", "Guernsey" and "Elmville", built 1889 and 1890) showed, it was claimed (NDM 10/12/1894), a "remarkable absence of corrosion". Another of his patents which was to achieve commercial success was his Feed Water Evaporator of 1892, reviewed in "The Engineer" of 7th October that year.

The shipyards of William Gray won their fourth Blue Riband in 1895 - this time again with 20 ships launched - all engined by Central Marine.

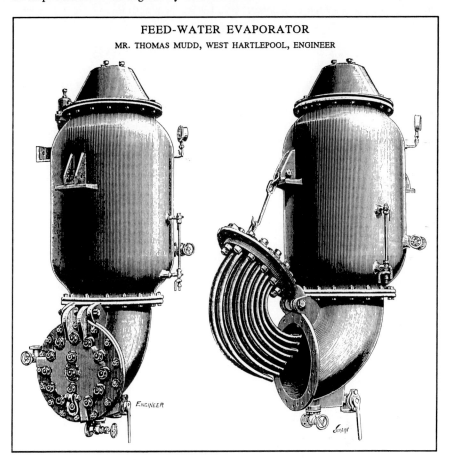

FEED-WATER EVAPORATOR
MR. THOMAS MUDD, WEST HARTLEPOOL, ENGINEER

## ENGINE NUMBERING SYSTEM.

Shipbuilders and engine builders rarely start numbering their production from 1, for obvious reasons, but CMEW was an exception. The numbering system adopted, which may be seen from the list of engines appended to this book, was to start from 1, and after Gray's Yard No. 501, to adopt the Yard Number as the engine number for Gray-built vessels - for other customers the older series of numbers was continued, as plenty of scope had been left after the change for Gray vessels, which took place in 1895 with s.s. "Argo".

The early engine numbers have been recorded in a small manuscript book which must have been started around the turn of the century and gives a later name for many of the earlier ships, not the original name; hence some effort has been entailed in achieving the correct allocation of some engine numbers below 290. A few are still doubtful, and marked as such in the listing. Identifiable non-marine engines have been included in the ship list, for the sake of completeness; these include hauling engines for railway inclines and engines for the London Electric Power Co., as well as Central Marine's own triple expansion driven power plants (three in number) and a set for the pumps in a French oil depot.

# WORKS EXTENSIONS & LARGER ENGINES.

In 1890 a 'shingling shop' was added to the new forge, as CMEW's expertise in wrought iron forgings was attracting substantial business: the renewed forge building itself was the large trussed-roof building bought from an exhibition site in Belgium, and at the time said to have (at 85 feet) the widest clear span of any building in Europe. It was 500 feet long and 36 feet to the eaves. The Company had developed a reputation in working wrought iron forgings, and at that time and for many years to come was able to secure orders and sub-contracts from many customers.

CMEW built their largest engine to date for the Furness-owned "Cambrian": this was a triple of 4000 IHP, with the LP cylinder 86 inches across, and a stroke of 54 inches. Service speed was 14 knots.

The press release at the end of 1897 showed 22 vessels engined (1896 - 18), including the "Rex" for liner service Sweden-Germany with a triple of 1800 IHP to give her 16 knots - a very high speed indeed for those days. Boiler output of 60 boilers included 21 additional to those in the 22 ships engined; there had been changes in the boiler shops to take advantage of the wider plates now available. Even large boilers could now be made "in one strake in the length of the boiler, thus avoiding all rivets under the bottom of the boiler".

Cliff House Workers about 1882 *(Courtesy of Hartlepool Museums Service)*

In December 1897, when trade was slack (there had been a dispute in the engineering industry during the year), working hours were temporarily reduced to 32½ per week, with no Saturday work . Business must have improved, for in May 1898 the Company announced a "Record Pay-out" for the whole William Gray organisation; the total weekly wage payment was £10,892, of which £2,812 was paid at CMEW.

Grays' fifth Blue Riband for yard output was won for the 1898 production of 25 ships, all but one of which were engined by Central Marine; the odd one by Blairs of Stockton, a major engine builder at this time, and this level of building, added to outside orders, led to a continued strong demand on the Central Marine forging capacity. This may well have been the reason for the 1898 acquisition of the Milton Forge & Engineering Co. of Greatham Street, West Hartlepool. The following year the firm acquired Cliff House Foundry, Mainsforth Terrace, from John Muir & Co.. Cliff House continued as part of CMEW to the end, and was noted for (inter alia) its line of haematite iron castings, for which South Durham Steel & Iron Co. was a steady customer. The press release of 1898 listed 29 ships engined by Central Marine, with a total IHP over 47,000: three of the engine sets were "unusually large, for the Atlantic trade". These vessels needed 65 CMEW boilers and a further 10 boilers were also sold. The large amount of work in hand "includes a repetition of Mr. Mudd's patent five-crank engines as fitted to the s.s. Inchmona".

Grays' Blue Riband No. 6 was awarded to the shipyards in 1900 for an output of 23 vessels, all of which were fitted with machinery from Central Marine, which by this time had a workforce reported as numbering 2000 men.

Typical Triple with Y-frames.

The Company's 1903 report showed that 16 sets of marine machinery had been installed, including 31 associated boilers, plus 6 boilers for renewals in older vessels. The report continued with the news that "the experience gained with very high boiler pressures (257 pounds) had allowed further progress in the provision of the economic addition of the 'Borrowman' Patent Superheating Apparatus to the boilers of ordinary cargo steamers.... with satisfaction to the owners of steamers."

Even in 1904 there were ships with compound (and even simple) engines needing more up-to date machinery: Central Marine installed a triple expansion set in the British cable ship "Minia". She had been built in Glasgow in 1866, before even the compound engine was widely accepted, so was already 38 years old when the new engine was fitted.

## APPOINTMENT OF MAURICE GIBB.

W. C. Borrowman, successor to Thomas Mudd, left the Company in 1907, and his position was filled by Maurice Sylvester Gibb, another very able engineer, who was a nephew of Sir George Gibb, a noted engineer of his day. M. S. Gibb had been apprenticed at Central Marine, after which he went to sea for some years. He came back to C.M.E.W. from the North Eastern Railway, which he had served as Machinery Superintendent. 1907 was not a good year for the Works: 13 ships engined (all triples, of 24,050 IHP in total), compared with the 1906 output of 24 sets (38,250 IHP). The December 1907 press report showed 28 boilers for the new ships engined, and 17 other boilers for various customers, including the Admiralty and the North Eastern Railway. A "special type of high-grade donkey boiler" had been a feature of the year's production. The foundry and drop forge had been well employed, and "additional machines had been laid down to meet the ever increasing demand".

The Franco-British Exhibition of 1908 in London was used to show a range of Central Marine products, including castings, forgings and auxiliaries. Perhaps the several sets of engines sent to France in 1908 and later years (almost all as castings) were a result from that promotion of the firm's products. In 1910 the "Marine Engineer" announced that Central Marine's new and improved evaporator was on the market.

Maurice Sylvester Gibb

In 1911 one of Mudd's non-marine patents had continued its appeal, as the press was informed that over 200 hopper-bottom rail wagons had now been fitted with Mudd's patent 'Quadrant' bottom doors, and about that time a further engine (No. 245) was built for electric power generation in the works. This engine was a triple of 900 HP and replaced the "Bradgate" engine. It drove a 500 kW B.T.H. generator supplying direct current to the works. Cliff House Foundry, which had proved a useful addition to the Works' casting capacity, was extended and modernised. Engines, auxiliaries, forged items and foundry products (both ferrous and non-ferrous) were exhibited at a major trade fair in Manchester in 1911.

In the same year the tug "Ponderoso" left the U.K. for the long trip to Valparaiso where she was to serve - CMEW had supplied the boilers, but the engines were by Crabtree.

Marmont Warren, a highly qualified Marine Engineer, who had his Extra Chief's ticket, joined Central Marine in 1912 as Assistant Works Manager, and was promoted to Works Manager in 1913 when Archie Henderson retired. Having served his time at CMEW (though his earlier education had been at Bradford), and had considerable sea-going experience, he was very well qualified for the post there, in temperament as well as technical ability. He stayed at the works until retirement many years later, although, according to his grandson D. N. Williams, he twice considered leaving - first when tempted by Richardsons Westgarth, and again when he and some associates were considering buying out Cliff House Foundry in the early 1920's. Both times, it is said, Sir William persuaded him to stay in post.

George Baines died in 1913 at Folkestone, en route for the South of France for the sake of his health, and it seems that his position of "Financial Manager" was never filled after his death. The Engine Works was, throughout its existence, a subsidiary company of William Gray & Co. Ltd., though it was customary for the General Manager of the engine works to be appointed to the parent company's board.

In 1913 CMEW were advertising "Multiple expansion engines on 3, 4 or 5 cranks".

Children at the gate with fathers' bait! *(Courtesy of Hartlepool Museums Service)*

# THE FIRST WORLD WAR.

The outbreak of War in August 1914 meant that the Works had to race to complete contracts to which it was already committed, and at the same time find capacity for urgent Admiralty or Ministry work. As war had begun to seem almost inevitable at least one shipowner had placed an order with Gray's shipyard at a premium price for early delivery: he had foreseen that a ship might well be very profitable in the event of an European War; the due completion of such a contract would be important to Grays and Central Marine, to avoid loss of the substantial premium the owner had offered.

When the standard ship programme got under way both the engine works and the shipyards were extremely busy helping to replace the war losses of merchant ships. A number of naval patrol craft were given turbine machinery of 3500 SHP; these were the first turbines from Central Marine (Engine No. 877 was the first). And, of course, many reciprocating steam engines were turned out, including some for a number of Gray-built monitors for the Navy. Small triples were built for three concrete-hulled tugs built at Amble and Sunderland; these were of 720 IHP. Some contracts one might not have expected to see were triples for cargo vessels built at the Euskalduna Shipyard, Bilbao (Engine Nos. 240-244 & 246); it seems probable that the hulls were towed to Hartlepool for engine installation. (Spain was a neutral country).

Work for the Shipping Controller was centred mainly on engining merchant vessels built by the parent company, although some ships came from other yards on Tyne, Wear and Tees. These were of several standard types, denominated by letters of the alphabet, and included some tankers of 8460 DWT, though the majority were dry cargo vessels of 4100 to 8300 DWT.

Mark Scurr was the Machine & Fitting Shop Superintendent from some date unknown until about the end of World War I, and was succeeded by William Oliver. This was an extremely important post, and there is no doubt that the succession of men appointed to it at Central Marine were excellent choices.

The Cowans & Sheldon cantilever crane which replaced the 80-ton sheerlegs on the quay was commissioned in 1916, in the period when the N.E.R. was widening the lock-gates to 70 feet. It was convenient to drop the old sheer-legs into the North Basin while that was drained for the alteration of the gates. The new crane's lifting capacity was 100 tons at 85 feet radius and 60 tons at 121 feet. The light hoist was able to lift 10 tons at 125 feet radius.

In the 1914-18 conflict women were employed for the first time on the shop floor, particularly for war production: Miss Winnie Sivewright, elder daughter of the well-known Naval Architect George W. Sivewright (of the Furness, Withy shipyard, Hartlepool) was brought in as Women's Supervisor. Miss Sivewright, who was a strong character and somewhat eccentric, was to fill the role once more in the 1939-45 War, and is the subject of many anecdotes. The Company was in the course of building new and larger boiler shops in 1914, but did not get the use of them for some time, as they were taken over in 1916 by the Ministry of Munitions for the production of 8-inch H.E. shells from forgings, using machinery supplied by the Ministry. These operations were by "The Hartlepools National Shell Factory" (Chairman Sir Wm. Gray), with a staff of 85 men and 365 women. Output over the 16 months of production was 81,346 shells - enough to last but a few minutes in any of the major artillery barrages on the Western Front during that conflict - and the cost per shell stated to be the second lowest in national rankings. In 1917 King George V and Queen Mary visited the shipyards and engine works: pictorial cover of that event includes photographs showing the women munition workers at Central Marine.

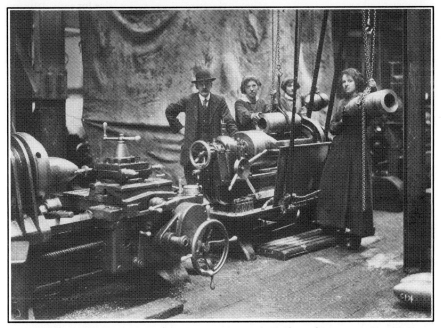

Women workers producing shells. *(Courtesy of Hartlepool Museums Service)*

During the later years of the War Maurice Gibb was drafted away from Hartlepool for twelve months to be the representative of the Ministry of Munitions in the unique 'Elizabethville' ammunition factory at Birtley, which was entirely staffed by Belgian refugees. For his work there Gibb was awarded the C.B.E.

G. B. Butler has drawn the author's attention to the fact that the Ministry had been over-optimistic on the level of hull production in a number of yards for tugs and barges, as well as other ships, so when the War ended there were surplus engines offered on the market. It would appear that CMEW engines Nos. 256 and 257 were built for concrete tugs never produced and these engines were later installed in the Swan, Hunter vessels "Dewstone" and "Bluestone" in 1922-23. This subject of the eventual destinations of spare engines from war production would itself make an interesting study.

J. B. Williams, Assistant Works Manager, died in 1919, and was followed by Mr. Webber.

## 1920 - 1929.

1920 was the year of Central Marine's first direct reduction geared turbine installation in a merchant vessel, and a number of guests were formally invited to the dock steaming trials (in the North Basin) of the "City of Adelaide" (Ellerman City Line vessel - Yard & Engine

Fitter A. Hartland working on a H.P. turbine rotor.
*(Courtesy of Hartlepool Museums Service)*

No. 939). This was the first of a series of Parsons-type turbine sets fitted in cargo-liner ships built by Grays at Hartlepool and in the Egis Yard at Sunderland: this latter, founded in 1917 on the south bank of the Wear, was operated by Grays for a consortium composed of Ellermans, Grays, Inchcape and Stricks - the name was an early acronym. Four merchant ships were turbine-fitted in 1920 and a further four in the very depressed year of 1921, when total engine output was down to 7 sets, though there was a considerable output of forgings, boilers, auxiliaries, etc. The Miners' Strike of 1921 had exacerbated the Company's difficulties at a time of depression in the marine industry.

By now the Company had its own established line of "CMEW" auxiliaries - pumps of all kinds, condensers, evaporators, feed-water heaters, de-aerators and so on, as well as ash-hoists and ash-ejectors - the latter items were of course necessary in coal-burning steamers.

Quadruple Expansion Engine.

In 1922, with the post-war slackness in shipping, due to depressed freight markets, sales were down to 5 sets of marine engines, but other business included "a number of Thermo-Couple installations", dockgate machinery, marine boilers, pumps, feed heaters, stern frames and other forgings, and also filters. The "Thermo-couple" device was a new type of pyrometer installed for measuring the temperature in boiler uptakes, superheaters and so on. Calibration of these instruments was the task of Mr. Pattison, Works Chemist for many years, and predecessor of Mr. Robinson. Another of Pattison's claims to fame was the ingenious and successful use of a mercurial ointment to prevent the seizing of steel nuts to their studs in high-temperature situations, such as superheaters and drop valves: this unguent was obtained in considerable quantities from a local pharmacist relative of his, but collected from the York Road shop with some diffidence, not to say embarrassment, by those apprentices who had learned of the medical condition for which it was more usually prescribed.

About this time the company started making a steam-driven compressor for creating and circulating cold air for cargo cooling, but it was an inefficient device and described by Bill Ryder (who suffered at sea with one) as a maintenance nightmare.

Sir William Cresswell Gray, Bt., died in 1924, and both his baronetcy and his role in the William Gray/Central Marine business were inherited by his son William, who had returned safely from army service in World War I.

In 1929 much was made of the launch of the "City of Dieppe" by Mrs. Jane Cambridge, the wife of one of the most senior shipyard employees. This was the Gray's Yard Number 1000. The press release asserted that CMEW had by then built 774 sets of engines, equal to 1.5 million IHP, and 2126 boilers, in addition to a very substantial output of forgings, auxiliaries, and many other items. After the launch the entire workforce was given tickets for an early "talkie" at a local cinema - Al Jolson starring in "The Singing Fool". Some of the author's older collaborators recall that occasion very clearly.

s.s. "City of Dieppe" (Gray 1000). *(Courtesy of A. Duncan, Gravesend)*

In the same year (1929) the Works engined the Gray-built "Brookwood" with Engine No. 1017 - described as having an "Exhaust Turbine and Steam Compressor". So far as can be seen from what records still exist, this type of installation does not seem to have been repeated from Central Marine, although other engine builders were installing the similar Swedish 'Gotaverken' type, which used the exhaust steam to raise the pressure of the steam between the High Pressure and Intermediate Pressure cylinders in a triple expansion engine. The makers of these devices claimed that they led to substantial economies in fuel, but they never became popular, probably on account of the maintenance implications.

"The Times" of 1st August 1929 carried a report of Ropners' "Swiftpool" coming to Hartlepool to be fitted by Central Marine to burn pulverised coal in her boilers. The installation merited a lengthy description in the "Marine Engineer & Motorship Builder" of September 1929. The suppliers of the equipment were the Brand Powdered Fuel System, Ltd - a company of which Sir George Buchanan and the Duke of Montrose were directors. The system included an on-board mill so that the vessel was not dependent on shore supplies of pulverised coal, and Arthur Lowery, with personal experience, recalls the continuous noise from the mill in the 'tweendeck. At the official lunch after the ship had been put on show in Hartlepool William Ropner is quoted as saying:- "As far as the ordinary cargo vessel is concerned, competitors have failed to prove that oil is more economical."

The experiment cannot have been much of a success, as there are no further records of CMEW fitting the "Brand" equipment. One informant states that the system was abandoned because of coal-dust explosions on vessels so fitted. A Glasgow-built vessel (s.s. "Berwindlea") had been converted to pulverised fuel by another yard shortly before the "Swiftpool", using the same make of plant.

Grays were now building a type of ship which was loosely referred to as having "boilers on deck". In fact the boilers were in the 'tweendecks: this design of ship was adopted to reduce the length of the engineroom and give more underdeck space for cargo. The first was "Dunelmia" (Engine No. 1028), for West Hartlepool owners, which sailed from the port on 23rd October 1929. Many others followed, though production of this type was abandoned in 1940 until after the war emergency; those which have been definitely identified are marked in the list of ships engined with the letters "TD".

Employees of those times recall clear memories of Marmont Warren as Works Manager. He was a well-known figure in the town - and even better known in the works, where he took a twice daily promenade with his Works Superintendent, William Oliver, after entering the workshops via the Gallery, where Arthur Dunn was the first foreman he met on his rounds. Woe betide anyone who was observed not to be very actively engaged in some form of toil when the duo came round ! A 1940's apprentice describes Marmont Warren sitting at his desk looking like Buddha, and he was certainly treated by the workforce with considerable respect, as was William Oliver. The latter, whose craggy appearance was most impressive, seemed able to be everywhere at once, and had an uncanny ability to detect any misdemeanour. Never one to suffer fools gladly, he was a keen disciplinarian, as no doubt he needed to be in that environment. Those were the days when Foremen and upwards wore bowler hats as a mark of rank.

One of the Pyman companies, for whose "Enfield" Central Marine's first engine had been supplied, took delivery of the "Welcombe" from Grays in 1930 (Yard and Engine No. 1034 - quadruple expansion of 421 NHP, 2271 IHP) and the local "Northern Daily Mail" of 26th

Light Machine Shop 1928

March gave extensive coverage to the history of the event under the headline "Engine No. 1 and No. 1034".

As the recession of 1929-33 deepened there was a serious shortage of work at Central Marine, and although the forge was rarely without orders, the rest of the works was more or less closed down in the worst times. An order from the Admiralty to engine the survey ship HMS "Challenger" must have been very welcome in 1931: the engine (probably No. 268) was sent to Chatham Dockyard. But the yard had disappointments such as that when a vessel ordered by a Norwegian shipowner was never taken up after the Owner was killed in a motoring accident - eventually the ship (Yard No. 1045) was traded by Grays for some years before she was sold.

Central Marine was not slow in testing new ideas. An "improved" propeller, with a larger than usual boss, was put before them by a Scandinavian designer, and a prototype of this was made in 1931-32. Sea trials took place, but with disappointing results, according to Arthur Frankland. The vessel's forward speed was far lower than had been claimed, and the propeller actually performed better going astern than ahead - a capability so little in demand that the new design was NOT adopted.

Some additional work was created by securing a licence to manufacture the Fleming Patent Lifeboat Propulsion Gear: the boat's propeller was driven by reciprocating handles. An attempt was made to link in a small diesel engine which could be started by the Fleming Gear, but this modification was not a success, and was dropped, although the basic hand-operated gear provided a modest extra workload for the foundry, forge and machine shops for some years.

# THE 'QUADROPOD' ENGINE.

By 1932 the first "Quadropod" engine had been developed enough for sale and was revealed to the technical press. This was a CMEW patent - a four-cylinder quadruple expansion steam engine with its 12 'double-beat type drop valves' serving all cylinders, and described as "Hush-hush" by the local press. It was claimed to be smaller, simpler and more economical than any comparable engine: the placing of the valves 'behind' the engine was an aid to compactness. The three boilers supplied steam at 260/280 p.s.i.g., and consumption was claimed to be 1 lb. of good coal per IHP per hour: forced draft (Howden), 180 (F) degrees of superheat from smoke-tube superheaters and CMEW air pre-heaters were all fitted as aids to fuel economy, together with two feed heaters to raise boiler feed-water to a high temperature. All this information (and more) is to be found in an illustrated article in "Engineering" of 22nd July 1932. There was a short run of vessels fitted with this new engine - first "Kepwickhall" and "Siltonhall", then "Hartington" "Hartismere" and "Hartlepool" (all 1932), after which there were no more until "Boltonhall" in 1935.

In contrast to these developments the firm engined a new Pilot Cutter for the Tees ("B. O. Davies") with a small triple of a mere 64 NHP - cylinders of 11", 18.25" and 30" - stroke 22". (Engine No. 1058)

About this time CMEW was licensed for the manufacture of the Michel patent thrust-block for propeller shafts. When the Michel inspectors came to examine the early production they were much impressed by the high standard of workmanship, and expressed their approval to the machinist mainly responsible, congratulating him on the quality of his work.

Quadropod Engine

1934 was a lean year, so the works was more than pleased to have a run of Ropner steamers arriving, occasionally three or four at a time, for conversion to superheat - this was called an 'improvement programme', and the cost was £4,000 per ship.   In all 48 units of the Ropner fleet were so 'improved', in the interest of achieving better fuel economy, even with bunker coals of lower quality than "Best Welsh".

Another 1934 task for CMEW was the building of two diagonal triples for the paddle ferries "Tattershall" Castle and "Wingfield Castle", and fitting feathering paddle wheels to these craft.    These engines appear to have been the first (and only) sets from the works for paddle propulsion.    The latter ship, now restored, is in the ''Historic Ships'' display at Hartlepool.

Maurice Gibb retired in 1936, and moved south, having been appointed to manage a new ''quango'' for industrial development in the North .   His place was taken by "Captain" Jack H. Farmer, who was to reign as General Manager for the next ten years.   One of the pieces of new plant put in about this time was a heavy gas-cutting profiling machine for the manufacture of such items as crank webs, previously cut out with a bandsaw and then milled or ground to shape: this installation greatly speeded what had been a very slow and labour-intensive task.

"Wingfield Castle" arrives home to Hartlepool in 1986 for restoration.
*(Courtesy of Hartlepool Borough Council)*

The Government gave some help to Shipping with two "Scrap & Build" Schemes - one in 1935 and one in 1939. Grays obtained one order under the first scheme and three under the second, and these orders meant work for Central Marine. A number of shipowners made applications for ships to be built by Grays at West Hartlepool, but some of these failed to get approval, either because the Owners could not find a ship to scrap, or because their capital position did not, in the eyes of the Committee, warrant a loan or grant. The ships ordered under the "Scrap & Build" programmes are identified in the list of vessels engined: the official report on the schemes gives the cost of the ships concerned - information which is often hard to find.

The works' own power station was closed down in 1936, and from that date the national grid supplied the electricity to the works. As much of the machinery was still driven by direct-current motors the grid supply had to be rectified for them, and the heavy current demand required a bank of very large rectifiers, able to deliver a total of 3,200 amperes direct current at 250 volts.

p.s. "Wingfield Castle"; restored C.M.E.W. Boilers. *(Courtesy of Hartlepool Museums Service)*

By 1937 the exhaust turbine was an established economy for the triple-expansion engine, and CMEW fitted this device first to the "Malvernian" (Engine No. 1072) - several more similar installations followed. This low-pressure turbine, which could be coupled on to the main shaft when appropriate, utilised the further expansion still remaining in the exhaust steam, and it was claimed that it could give an extra knot of speed with no adverse effect on bunker consumption.

A new type of drop valve was fitted in the triples of the "Oakdene" of 1936 (Engine No. 1071) and the "Felldene" of 1937 (Engine No. 1062). The Admiralty appeared once more in the order book in 1937: Grays built two survey ships ("Gleaner" and "Hazard") and both were fitted with CMEW Turbines.

At this time the Works had a show-case of warwick-screws, eyebolts and other small items from the forge in the Central Station, Newcastle: the date when it was first put up and the date of its disappearance seem to be lost in the mists of time.

## THE SECOND WORLD WAR.

Up to this point the machine shops had been using machine tools that were, in the main, old but still serviceable. The urgent need for output was the spur to acquiring a good deal of new plant of various kinds for the light and heavy machine shops as well as the foundry and other sections of the works.

During the 1939-45 War, as in the 1914-18 conflict, women were employed at CMEW, and Miss Winnie Sivewright, JP, returned to the Works once more in her role as supervisor for the female staff on the shop-floor: she was no less eccentric in her second spell with Central Marine than in her first tour of duty. Mrs. Olive Lowes (formerly Elliott), relates how she started at age 16 in the machine shop where the foreman (Taffy Turner) ruled the girls with what she describes as a rod of iron. Later she moved to the tube plate drilling

Women workers W.W.II. (Centre front Miss W. Sivewright) *Courtesy of Mrs. O. Lowes*

machine in Arthur Tate's shop, and on the next machine was ''little Alfie Manners'', father of "Battling Manners".   She speaks of the strictness and yet the kindness of Miss Sivewright, who somehow managed to obtain , on a fairly regular basis, the occasional rabbit: she would ride her ancient bicycle to the houses of 'her girls' and each would, in turn, receive this welcome addition to the wartime rations.

The formidable William Oliver retired in 1942: many of those who had most feared him in their youth readily acknowledge his ability, the control he exercised, and the contribution he made to Central Marine.   He was succeeded by the Fitting Shop Foreman, J. O. Lumsden ("Ossie"), who later rose to fill the vacancy created by "Monty" Warren's retirement and become Works Manager: only the third man to occupy that important post, and a worthy successor to Henderson and Oliver.

Heavy demands were once more made on Central Marine production by the needs of war, and a great deal of overtime was worked in order to increase output.   The introduction of wartime standard types of ship ("Empire" ships) was quite early in this conflict, and CMEW was to produce engines for those built by Grays - in standard types, like the ships. A lower standard of finish was agreed, known as "war finish", though the basic high standard of propelling and auxiliary machinery was maintained.   Some of the very old machines in the shops were replaced by more up to date plant such as borers and turret lathes, which allowed higher productivity.

Grays' yards built cargo ships of 9650 DWT and 10,350 DWT, also vessels equipped with heavy-lifting gear for handling tanks and landing craft ("Empire Malta", etc.) as well as colliers and 24 ships of the type known as "Scandinavian", well suited to timber-carrying as well as other bulk cargoes.   All these ships had CMEW triple expansion machinery, and, of course, CMEW boilers and auxiliary machinery.

A minor disturbance to life in the workshops came in 1943, with the "Apprentices' Strike" and their demand for dismissal of a foreman   (Arthur Tait) whom some of the boys considered to be unreasonably harsh.   One who has understandably vivid memories of this incident is Allen ('Dixie') Dunn, perhaps the only participating apprentice whose father was a Foreman at Central Marine at the time.   The strike seems to have been fomented by one particular young man who was later released from his reserved occupation and allowed to join the R.A.F.

The indentures entered into by apprentices and their parents or guardians precluded them from taking any part in a strike, so their walk-out was a rather dramatic occasion.   The Works' Shop Stewards had assured the Apprentices that the men would come out in sympathy, but that assurance proved totally without foundation.   There was, of course, never any hope that they could secure their demands, and after a few days they came back: the management had fully supported a valued and effective foreman.   Each offending apprentice had to appear before Mr. Warren and eat humble pie - their memories of that are very clear indeed, as Marmont Warren, though quite softly-spoken, was a formidable figure to these young men, even when not wearing his bowler hat.

Output in 1943-44 included a number of small two cylinder compound engines for some of the many TID tugs which were produced:  the main hull builder for these was Richard Dunston of Hessle.   The boilers did not come from Central Marine, but the propellers did. It has not proved possible to discover with any certainty how many were built at Hartlepool;  anecdotal evidence indicates ten or twelve such engines being carefully packed and sent away to the builders of the tugs, but the run of engine numbers with no ship name shown suggests there may have been about eighteen. These little engines were apparently made under a sub-contract, possibly from Dickinsons of Sunderland, and the tugs were unfortunately of too low gross tonnage to be included in Lloyd's Register. Sub-contracts create difficulties for the maritime historian. (Only two identified tug engines are included in the list.)

s.s. "Boltonhall", built by Grays in 1935 with a Quadropod engine came back in 1943 to have a new triple expansion engine fitted. It appears that the same boilers were retained, but without superheat, and the steam pressure was reduced from 260 to 225 pounds per sq. inch.

Mr. Marmont Warren
*(Courtesy of Mrs. E. Williams)*

The danger of enemy attack precluded normal sea-trials taking place during the War, and engine trials were carried out in the Basin. This was a source of great regret to senior apprentices, whose task was to take indicator cards during engine trials, so those who were serving in the Drawing Office as the War was ending were delighted when the chance came for a sea-trip on duty during Builders' trials prior to the delivery of the ship to her Owners. Some of them then discovered that they were prone to 'mal-de-mer', and at least one senior manager standing under the cylinder platform narrowly missed being showered with evidence of that indisposition.

## POST-WAR OPERATIONS.

Once the War was over shipowners were anxious to replace their war losses as well as ageing ships, and Grays received multi-ship orders from British, Scandinavian and Greek owners. A number of these vessels had Bauer-Wach exhaust turbines added to their triple expansion engines: this German patent gave added economy by utilising the low pressure steam in a further expansion stage after it left the L.P. cylinder of the traditional triple. The steamer "Urlana" of 1946 had a triple with exhaust turbine, but that turbine was from Swan, Hunter and not CMEW.

In 1947 Ellermans had contracted with Henry Robb of Leith to build a number of new ships, and Central Marine obtained a contract to make triple expansion sets for four of those vessels (Engine Nos. 290-293). The reader will note the continuation of the engine numbering system adopted in 1895, by which the Yard Number was used for Gray-built vessels, and numbers in the lower series for sets supplied for other ships.

Although there had been steady progress in motorising machines in the shops, the works still had a number of line shafts from which belt-drive was taken for some items of plant. A further post-war improvement much welcomed by the workforce was the installation of flush toilets in the works to replace the earth closets installed in 1884 - the new cesspit drained into the Slake.

C.M.E.W. Machine Shop 1950. *(Courtesy of Hartlepool Museums Service)*

Fitting Furnace Fronts. *(Courtesy of Hartlepool Museums Service)*

J. H. Farmer retired in 1946, and Samuel Hamilton Dunlop ("Hamil") was recruited from Harland & Wolff to replace him as General Manager in overall control of Central Marine - a position he held until the closure of the Works 16 years later, and was later also to be Production Manager for the Company's shipbuilding activities. The administrative structure remained as it had always been, with the William Gray & Co. main Board at the top, and the General Manager answerable to that Board. Marmont Warren moved up from Works Manager to Assistant General Manager in 1946.

In the immediate post-war years the Works had many orders from Smith's Dock, Middlesbrough for boilers to be fitted into whale-catchers, a type of ship in which that yard specialised. The majority of these boilers had the "Deighton" corrugated furnace, one of the three types in common use. Another type was the "Morison", invented on the other side of the North Basin at Richardsons. The Works was offering Scotch boilers producing steam at 180 to 250 p.s.i.g. and Water Tube boilers (Babcock & Wilcox type) of 250 to 590 p.s.i.g. with an evaporative capability of 17,000 to 30,000 lbs/hour.

## GRAY-POLAR DIESELS.

In 1947, after a Board decision to seek a licence from the makers of Polar-Atlas diesel machinery, there were visits to Nydquist & Holm AB., (Nohab) of Trollhattan, Sweden, to negotiate successfully for licence rights. These medium speed diesels (running at up to 250 r.p.m.) were thought to be suitable for the types of merchant ships built by Grays' operation: the engines were lighter, smaller and more compact than the slow-speed engines

Gray - Polar Diesel Engine. *(Courtesy of Hartlepool Museums Service)*

such as Doxfords. The power to weight ratio was good. Standardised cylinder units meant it was available in sizes of 4 to 9 cylinders (1580-3550 BHP for a single engine) and up to 4500 BHP for two engines geared and flexibly coupled to one shaft. As soon as the licence was secured, a test-bed was set up for the Gray-Polar engines, with the necessary ancillary equipment and a dynamometer able to take the output of engines up to eight cylinders.

The view of Steve Pearson, who worked on redesigning parts of the engine, was that the Swedish designers had not fully developed the engine at that time. CMEW did a lot of remedial work on the Polar, including complete re-design and change of material for cylinder heads to obviate cracking, and might well have made more progress in improving the reliability of the Gray-Polar diesel, but by the time this was near the engines had acquired an unfortunate reputation, and for that and other reasons the demand for them was minimal. One well-documented visit to the Polar factory at Trollhattan was made in November 1953 by Messrs. Eric Rutherford and S. K. Pearson of Central Marine, who were joined by Messrs. Mumford and MacDonald from J. G. Kincaid's of Glasgow, also Polar licensees. The purpose of the trip was to witness the tests of the new M60T engine, to discuss CMEW's problems with the engines they had built, and to report what progress they had made in Hartlepool towards finding solutions. Nohab appeared to take on board the points made by the Hartlepool team, and further technical co-operation was agreed.

The Gray-built "Spigerborg" of 1950, for Danish owners, had been the first vessel fitted with a Gray-Polar engine and was fully described in "The Shipping World" of March 15th, 1950. She had a 7-cylinder unit, two stroke single-acting, with cylinders of 500 mm diameter and stroke of 700 mm (Yard & Engine No. 1234). The service rating was 2145 BHP at 195 rpm, and the daily consumption was 11.4 tons of diesel fuel. There was a reduction gearbox to the propeller shaft.

m.v. "Spigerborg" of 1950. *(Courtesy of Hartlepool Museums Service)*

Whatever had been or might have been done in the way of development, the engine would remain a medium-speed type, still needing a reduction gearbox, and, as a trunk piston type of engine, was not really suited to burning heavy oil. The usual requirement of shipowners was for a power unit which was as simple and as low-maintenance as possible, also economical (and that could mean having the ability to run on the cheapest suitable fuel). It seems that the Gray-Polar licence was not dropped, and the engine would have been available at any time up to the Works closing, but there was no serious demand for it in the cargo ship field at that time. The ore-carrier "Oreosa", built in 1954 and engined with Gray-Polar diesels, was still sailing in 1988: Steve Pearson reports that Lloyd's Register shows she still had the original engines after 34 years.

m.v. "Oredian" sistership of our "Oreosa". *(Courtesy of Hartlepool Museums Service)*

The steam technology which had been the Works' main field until 1947 was less sophisticated and demanding than the diesel field, and it became necessary to expand the research and test facilities for the Gray-Polar. A four-cylinder Polar engine was kept in the shops for test purposes, and this proved invaluable in the development work, of which much was needed, as the engine was one which had "grown" from the original Atlas non-marine engine. The recurrent problems with cylinder heads meant the despatch of spares by air to many parts of the world: solutions for these were worked on in Sweden, but also tackled locally on two fronts - in the drawing office, where Eric Rutherford and his team re-designed it, and in the metallurgical laboratory where Ernest Pigott worked on a new material - a form of Spheroidal Graphite Iron which was very ductile. The double pronged attack finally solved the problem, but brought CMEW into conflict with Mond Nickel, who had an all-embracing patent on that material. Eventually CMEW were allowed to make their own "bendable cast iron", but only for their own use - they were not allowed to seek business in this material from outside clients.

This and other development work resulted in expansion of the chemical and metallurgical laboratory facilities, and the introduction (in the early 1950's) of radiographic test facili-ties (X-ray and Gamma ray) and a photo-elastic laboratory to examine the stresses in cast metal components. These departments worked under Ernest Pigott, Chief Chemist & Metallurgist, who had come from the Navy Laboratory in Sheffield, in succession to Robinson, previously Chief Chemist.

More new machine tools were installed in the early post-war years, including a 20-foot planer, and a Noble & Lund machine for crankshaft production: also a David Brown gear-cutting & milling machine, a slotting machine, and new milling cutters fitted to a planer of 1886, giving that venerable machine a new lease of life. The Iron Foundries were modernised in all aspects, including the sand & loam side. Foundry work is extremely dirty and shower facilities were built at CMEW and at Cliff House Foundry: men were, however, expected to shower in their own time before leaving. Bill Ryder, then Works Engineer, relates that many of the CMEW foundrymen declined to use their showers, but at Cliff House the showers were well-used, and some employees requested (and obtained) permission to bring their families to use them at weekends.

The year 1950 saw further improvements, when the Brass Foundry and Coppersmith's shops were converted from coke-fired stoves and furnaces to gas-fired.

## GRAY-DOXFORD DIESELS.

The shipyard customers' demand for low-speed diesel units led to a Board decision of 1952 to negotiate with the Sunderland firm of Doxfords for a licence for the local manufacture of Doxford diesel engines. Shipowners liked this well-tried and fully developed power unit, which could by now burn cheaper heavy oils without sulphurous sludge problems in the crankcase. Further, these low-speed units were directly coupled to the shaft, needing no gearing, and were available in a wide range of output power. Doxfords, satisfied that Central Marine had the plant and skills required, granted the licence. The Doxford test-bed was set up in 1953, and the first Gray-Doxford to be installed was Engine No. 1295 in m.v. "Degema" of 1959. Only five more Doxfords were built at Central Marine and these included the final main engine, No. 1307, for the ore-carrier "Mabel Warwick" of 1960. This ship was for Houlder Brothers of London, and was named after the wife of Walter C. Warwick, West Hartlepool born, who had started his career with Furness, Withy in Hartlepool and then moved to their London headquarters.

Gray-Doxford engines were offered either normally aspirated in a range from 4-cylinder (560mm x 2160 mm combined stroke) of 2200 BHP to 6-cylinder (700 mm x 2320 stroke) of 7200 BHP, or supercharged from 4-cylinder (600 mm x 2000 mm) of 4500 BHP to 6-cylinder (700 mm x 2320 mm) of 9500 BHP. All these engines had a claimed consumption

Gray-Doxford(s) in erecting shop. *(Courtesy of Hartlepool Museums Service)*

of 0.37 lbs/BHP/hour on normal diesel fuel and 0.384 lbs/BHP/hr on heavy oil. Shaft speeds were around 115 r.p.m. and the engine was directly coupled to the propeller shaft.

Lack of overhead clearance in the shop had necessitated the deepening of the engine erection pits by 3 to 6 feet to accommodate these taller engines, and the Doxford test-rig included a new dynamometer.

Gray-Doxford connecting rod being turned.

Ted Hunter milling water-cooling grooves in a Gray-Doxford engine cylinder liner.
*(Both photos above courtesy of Hartlepool Museums Service)*

# LATER DEVELOPMENTS.

Even in 1953 the steam triple was not completely obsolete, and s.s."Hallindene", Gray-built, was fitted with one, complete with exhaust turbine. In 1954 Grays built the "Stanpool" for London owners: while still on the stocks she was sold to the Soviet Government. She was broken up in Turkey in 1993, and "Sea Breezes" reported that her CMEW triple expansion engine (No. 1266) is to go to a museum in Istanbul.

s.s. "Hallindene" off Table Mountain, S.A. *(Courtesy of Hartlepool Museums Service)*

The enhanced welding techniques required for a contract from Spanner Boilers were trained for and in 1955 Lloyd's Class I welding was introduced into the Works. Local pride was boosted by the knowledge that CMEW had achieved this before their rivals across the North Basin - Richardsons, Westgarth.

In 1955 Marmont Warren retired from his post of Assistant General Manager, having (according to 'Fast Anchor' of 1956) spent a total of 53 years with Central Marine, and was succeeded by G. F. Scott, formerly Technical Manager. S. H. Dunlop's role was extended to being Production Director of the shipyards as well as of the engine works.

The pattern-shop - always an important section of an engine works - was re-tooled in 1956-7, as a further step in the post-war modernisation.

On Palm Sunday 1957 the 100-ton cantilever crane was in use for lifting boilers into a new vessel, and after the job was completed, the hook was raised: unfortunately the upper limit switch arm was distorted, and the rising block passed it, with the result that the motor did not cut out - the 8½" diameter shaft was bent, the drum bearings smashed and the drum pulled from its seating. Bill Ryder, who had earlier succeeded Claud Mallett as Works Engineer, was called out from a church service he was attending, and assembled a team to get the crane back into working order. After seven days work it was ready for re-testing, with the shipyard's bundles of "arrester chains" as weights for the test. The following year the accumulation of small movements in the king-post had so built up that the pinion which rotated the crane was coming out of mesh. The near 400 ton weight of the rotating head was taken on jacks, and the king-post securings cut. Careful measurement showed that what was needed was a movement of almost 2 inches along the line of the quay and over half an inch at right angles to that direction to ensure a perfect mesh. After that all was re-secured and the crane slewing was once more in perfect working order.

Those who have not been concerned with lifting machinery of that magnitude may have little conception of the task of renewing the main hoist rope in a crane like this tall 100-ton cantilever. The rope has to pass through multiple sheaves, and the new rope must be spliced to the old one to be pulled through - but spliced in such a way as to allow it to pass through the blocks: In this case it was necessary to make a splice 9 feet long so that it could be slender and flexible enough to follow the tortuous course required. Fortunately it was not a task that needed doing very often.

Even in the middle 1950's the day of the triple expansion steam engine was not over, and in 1955-56 Central Marine despatched two (Nos. 296 & 297) to other shipyards: these were fitted with an Exhaust Turbine for greater economy in service. Their final triple was for the Greek-flag "Lucy" (Engine No. 1285) in 1957 - a ship which came back only four years later, in 1961, to be re-engined with a Gray-Doxford (which was given Engine No. 298, as the Yard Number could hardly be used again).

Non-destructive testing facilities were further uprated in 1958 and 1959, and in 1958 Central Marine was building Pametrada designed turbines for the "Rose of Lancaster", followed in 1959 by similar engines for the "Mary Holt " (No. 1300). Superheated steam was supplied at 810 degrees Fahrenheit from Central Marine water-tube boilers.

t.s. "Rose of Lancaster". *(Courtesy of B. G. Spaldin, Hartlepool)*

Outside work was sought, and although the Technical Department had many ideas there was little basic experience in quoting for fabrication, machining and so on. Nevertheless, orders were secured from local works for boilers, process plant, steel fabrication, pressure vessels and castings. Among the new customers were I.C.I. and Head, Wrightson. Cliff House Foundry had for a long time been selling haematite iron castings to the local steelworks, and done other outside work as well. Unfortunately it was clearly not possible to achieve any volume of orders which could sustain the Central Marine operations.

One step taken in 1960 was the acquisition of the Evans Pump business from the South of England, and a number of general purpose pumps, mostly non-marine, were made and export sales were achieved. The Evans pumps were mostly of the centrifugal type, but some were reciprocating, and some had a gearbox supplied with them.

# LIQUIDATION.

The Engine Works had been established as an adjunct to the Gray shipbuilding activities, and although they had had numerous outside customers, many of whom returned with further orders, the level of business without Grays' shipyard output to engine was very unlikely to support the engine works and its ancillaries. By the end of the 1950's Grays were having serious difficulties in obtaining orders for ships: quite apart from other factors, there was the very serious limitation on the shipyards that they were all in a dock with a lock entrance of 70 feet wide. Thus the yards could not build ships of more than about 17,000 tons carrying capacity at a time when world demand was for ships of much larger size. It was not to be too long before ships of 35,000 tons carrying capacity would be known as "handy-sized bulkers". The years 1950 to 1980 were a period of most dramatic and extraordinary growth in ship sizes for both tankers and dry-bulk carriers.

By the start of 1962 the future of Central Marine was looking very bleak, and S. H. Dunlop was advising employees to look for alternative employment.

William Gray and Co. Ltd went into voluntary liquidation in December 1962, the shipyards closed, and the liquidators began the task of selling off the assets of the business. The remaining workforce was disbanded, with the inevitable consequent misery and distress. It was a heavy blow to the town to lose its remaining shipyard and marine engine building operation - the last marine engine from Richardsons, Westgarth (Hartlepool) had been produced in 1961.

Peat, Marwick & Mitchell were given the task of liquidation, represented by Rupert Nicholson. Central Marine was, as a wholly owned subsidiary of William Gray & Co. Ltd., necessarily involved in the liquidation. B. G. Spaldin records that at more or less the same moment the former s.s."Argyll", by now "San Luciano", built in 1892 and fitted with CMEW Engine No. 129, was being broken up after a useful life of 70 years.

Thus the demise of the shipyards meant the end for Cliff House Foundry and for Central Marine, too - the end for an engine works which had been set up, as the brass plate on the main offices proclaimed, to be "Marine Engineers, Boilermakers, Forgemasters, Iron & Brass Moulders, Coppersmiths and Brass Finishers". The works had produced well over 1,000 sets of propelling machinery, very large numbers of boilers, auxiliary machines and many, many other items. The name 'Central Marine' was known the world over in maritime circles, and their engines, auxiliaries and boilers had a first-class reputation.

s.s. "Argyll / "San Luciano" *(Courtesy of A. Duncan, Gravesend)*

The machinery was sold off by auction in early May 1963, the auction being conducted by Basil Noble, senior partner of Sanderson, Townend & Gilbert (Darlington). The final lift by the Cantilever Crane was some time after the end of the auction sale of the equipment: it consisted of a large Heenan & Froude Dynamometer, sold to Belgian buyers, and the author had the melancholy task of arranging the cranage into the exporting vessel on behalf of Belgian friends. The CMEW crane was later demolished, changing the skyline of that area of the docks for ever, but some of the engine works sheds, which had reverted to the lessors - the owners of the dock estate in a long succession from the N.E.R. - were converted to warehouses, and are still in use in 1995 for storage of paper, pulp and other imported commodities. Until 1992 one could still see the name of the works on one of the original buildings.

During the liquidation some members of the work-force were retained by the Liquidator to help with preparing for the auction sale of the assets - among them was Arthur Dunn, foreman of the Brass Finishing Shop. At this time most of the Central Marine records were incinerated: the Liquidator was, not unnaturally, interested in retaining only those things for which could he could expect to raise cash. However, some engine drawings from the period 1935 to 1962 have survived, and reached Hartlepool Museum Services in 1983 via Smith's Dock Co. Ltd.

# APPRENTICES.

The Engine Works had always taken apprentices; the numbers would vary with the commercial activity of the organisation, but around 100 in all at any one time seems to have been the level from the 1930's until the slow-down of the late 1950's. In the later years of the 19th century it was said that there would be a total number of apprentices in all the works in Hartlepool and West Hartlepool of near one thousand. One of the earliest must have been Alexander L. Mellanby, born 1871 in West Hartlepool, who went on to become Emeritus Professor of Civil and Mechanical Engineering at The Royal Technical College, Glasgow. He spent a year early in his career at Richardsons, across the basin from Central Marine.

Mr. Ernest Marples, Minister of Transport (right), steps out with Sir William Gray, Bart., Chairman of William Gray & Co. Ltd., at the start of a tour of the Shipyards and Engine Works. *(Courtesy of Hartlepool Museums Service)*

The majority of the former apprentices interviewed were of WW2 vintage, and many felt that they had been used as cheap labour under rather harsh conditions. The consensus was that the standard of training they received at that time was not very high, but this may well have been due to the heavy pressure on Central Marine to produce maximum output for the war effort. There was a great deal of overtime worked, both evenings and weekends, though some recognition was given, in a limited way, to the need for the apprentices to attend evening classes at the town's Technical College. In addition, many of them were enrolled into the Home Guard Company commanded by Sir William Gray, and this entailed further inroads into their limited free time. At least one described himself as "permanently tired" and on occasion able to sleep inside a boiler while the caulkers were busy on it with their hammers. Another reckons that he lost at least one third of his night school time due to overtime and Home Guard duties during those war years.

It is said to have been common practice for apprentices to be trained as 'engineers' at Central Marine, rather than as fitters or turners, and the synopsis of the training received by Jim Wilson from 1943 to 1948 certainly indicates that he was given useful, wide experience in the works and in the fitting-out department; the training was considered by this particular apprentice to have been well thought out, even allowing him to gain 'valuable knowledge and experience of other processes, although not directly involved in them'.

Many of the foremen were seen as inflexible and somewhat despotic: not at all unusual in industry at that time, but one must remember that these years were the young men's first industrial experience. Some Apprentices judged their seniors to be unwilling to consider new (and possibly better) ways of doing some tasks in the shops: perhaps the lean years of the early 1930's had something to do with that.

Those apprenticed around the second World War were given a hammer and a flat chisel (only) as their starting tool-kit, though a large square file was sometimes added. If they had to cut oil grooves in white metal bearings, then a round-nosed chisel would be added. One who complained about the quality of hammer and chisel with which he had been provided was told (by a foreman) that his course of action should be to "pinch someone else's tools".

A point of interest is that at least one of the foremen was singled out by most of the interviewees as more understanding and sympathetic than the others - this was Arthur Dunn, who worked in "The Gallery", the brass finishing section. As his own son Allen was one of the WW2 apprentices, perhaps this was why he looked more kindly on those who came into his charge, though he was certainly not at all understanding when the apprentices came out on strike, being concerned for his own position.

Another man who was particularly well thought of by his charges was draughtsman Charlie Morley, later Chief Estimator; he taught many of them at evening classes, where he lectured for many years, and this may well have been a factor in his attitude. The evening classes were highly spoken of, even in those difficult war years, and other tutors' names mentioned were those of Mr. Reid, the Principal, and Messrs. Gibbs and Gatenby: the latter was headmaster of another school in the town and yet taught at "night school".

Those who had experience of CMEW in the years after WW2 consider that much more effort was made to provide a wider and more effective training, particularly once the apprentices had reached the drawing office. Wide-ranging lectures every Monday afternoon, combined with technical films and other training aids, were clearly what Mr. S. H. Dunlop, General Manager, described in 1957 as

> "enlarging the facilities in these Works for the training of Apprentices . . . . . an attempt by the Management to provide . . . the thorough groundwork that is a necessity in order that young men can have the basic training to fully equip them for the many opportunities which the future presents."

He went on to express the hope that the wider training now being provided would in due course produce the key men needed for the making of the new and varied products which must eventually be undertaken by the Works.

As many men trained at CMEW have gone on to responsible engineering positions - some at sea and others ashore, including positions within the works - the training cannot have been by any means bad, even though some of them failed to get as full a range of experience in fitting and turning in the shops as they would have liked. It seems probable that they would have learned to improvise and to cope with some elderly machinery in their time. Those who came from relatively sheltered backgrounds, and there were quite a few, certainly suffered a culture shock in the apprenticeship, which would be a hard school at any time, but especially so in wartime, when the combined demands of long hours, overtime, night school and Home Guard (in Sir William Gray's company, of course) meant they were very stretched - even, as one war-time apprentice mentioned earlier records, 'permanently exhausted'. They certainly encountered some characters, and learned much about people.

The natural, but not inevitable, progression for many of the apprentices was to go to sea as junior engineers after the end of their indentures. Some stayed at sea as career marine engineers, while others came ashore after a spell of sea-faring and took shore jobs in engineering. The I.C.I. works at Billingham was, from its creation in the 1920's, something of a magnet for young engineers of the neighbourhood, and there was some doubt about the value I.C.I. placed on sea-time when they recruited engineering staff. This belief may well have affected the desire of some to follow the traditional route of starting their careers with a spell at sea.

When the closure of the works came there were still a few apprentices who had not finished their time, and the management made considerable efforts to find them places elsewhere for the completion of their period of training.

# SOURCES CONSULTED.

## Periodicals:

Northern Daily Mail, West Hartlepool

The Times

'Marine Engineer & Motorship Builder'

'The Engineer'

'Engineering'

'Steamship'

'Shipping World'

'The Shipbuilder'

'Marine Review'

'Sea Breezes'

'Marine Engineer & Naval Architect'

'Machinery Market'

'Railway Gazette'

## Published works:

B. G. Spaldin - "Shipbuilders of The Hartlepools" - (Hartlepool Borough Council 1986)

Robert S. Craig - "William Gray & Co., 1864-1913" (Ch. 9 of "Shipping Trade & Commerce" ed. Corfield & Aldcroft: Leicester Univ. Press 1981)

Lloyd's Registers 1887-88 onwards.

"Fast Anchor" (Wm. Gray & Co. Ltd. - House Magazine: Hartlepool Museum Service)

MacGibbon - "B.O.T. & Marine Engineering Knowledge", 10th Edn.

B. Mason (ed) "Encyclopaedia of British Shipping" 1908

T. Mudd "Central Marine Engine Works" Dec. 1886. (Transactions of North East Coast Institution of Engineers & Shipbuilders 1887

Ward's Directories of West Hartlepool.

"Who was Who"

## Other Sources:

Press cuttings books of W. Gray & Co. and Central Marine - Hartlepool Museums Service

Manuscript list of engine numbers - Hartlepool Museums Service

'Robert Wood', 'Ryder' and other collections - Hartlepool Museums Service

# ACKNOWLEDGEMENTS.

The author is grateful to Hartlepool Borough Council for having agreed to publish this history, and acknowledges with thanks the help and encouragement he has received from the following people, without whose assistance this book would have been the poorer :-

H. S. Appleyard, Wolviston: G. B. Atkinson, Hartlepool: S. Bradley,

Hartlepool: G. B. Butler, Stockton: R. S. Craig, Dover: A. E. Dunn, Hartlepool:

A. Frankland, Hartlepool: A. Jowsey, Armathwaite: W. H. Leck, Billingham:

A. Lowery, Hartlepool: Mrs. O. Lowes, Hartlepool: Mrs. M. Lumsden, Hartlepool:

C. B. Madderson, Dover: Dr. B. Newman, University of Newcastle-upon-Tyne:

B. Oxtoby, Kenilworth: H. Peacock, Hartlepool: S. K. Pearson, Hartlepool:

E. C. Pigott, Hartlepool: J. Plews, Cockermouth: W. Ryder, Hartlepool:

T. G. W. Saunders, Hartlepool: G. Shanley, Hartlepool: H. Short, Hartlepool:

R. Sowler, Whitby (now of Newton Aycliffe): B. G. Spaldin, Hartlepool:

T. F. Tritschler, Hartlepool: D. N. Williams, Hartlepool: S. J. Wilson, Hartlepool.

The staffs of Hartlepool Maritime Museum and the Reference Department of Hartlepool Central Library, who made available much material, including Yard Books, CMEW Engine Book, Grays' Press Cuttings File and other items. The staffs of the Science Museum Library, Middlesbrough Central Library and Newcastle-upon-Tyne Central Library, also of the Institute of Marine Engineers.

The author has found all those whom he approached to be enthusiastic in their wish to help in the assembly and collation of information for this project, and generous in their support of his efforts. He tenders his apologies to any participants whose names may have been accidentally omitted. It is to be regretted that a number of interesting reminiscences had to be left out of this history, but the information, comments and suggestions offered during its preparation have been invaluable.

# APPENDIX 'A'

Short version list of the engine output from C.M.E.W.
(with engine numbers as far as ascertained: a more detailed list has been
deposited with Hartlepool Maritime Museum and Hartlepool Central Library).

## KEY TO SHIPBUILDERS

| | | | |
|-----|-------------------------|------|------------------------------|
| AC | A. & C., Dunkirk | AFC | Amble Ferroconcrete |
| ARM | Armstrong, Whitw., Nwc | AST | A. Stephen, Ggw |
| AUS | S. P. Austin, Sld | AYR | Ayrshire Dockyard, Ayr |
| BC | Barclay, Curle, Ggw | BI | Burntisland S/Bldg. |
| BM | Bonn & Mees | CAL | Caledon, Dundee |
| CF | Caillard Freres | CHA | Chantiers Atlantique |
| CHF | Chantiers de France | CHN | Chantiers de Normandie |
| CNE | C. & N. Espanola | CT | Craig, Taylor, Stockton |
| EG | Egis Yard, Sunderland | EU | Euskalduna, Bilbao |
| EW | Edw. Withy, Hpool | FM | Forges de Mediterannee |
| FS | Flensburger Schiffbau | FW | Furness Withy, Hpool |
| HL | Hawthorn Leslie Nwc | HR | Henry Robb, Leith |
| IR | R. Irvine, W. Hpool | JB | J. Blumer, Sld |
| JL | J. Laing, Sld | LG | London & Greenock |
| LO | Londonderry S/Bldg | MI | Mitchell & Co. Nwc |
| NDC | Naval Dockyd, Chatham | NER | N. E. Railway |
| NW | New Waterway, Schiedam | OG | Osbourne Graham, Sld |
| P | Pickersgill, Sld | RD | Raylton Dixon, Mbro |
| RDU | Richard Dunston | SH | Swan Hunter, Nwc |
| SHT | Short Bros., Sld | SHWR | Swan & Wigham Richdson, Nwc |
| WC | Wear Concrete | WG | William Gray, W. Hpool |
| WR | Wigham Richdsn, Nwc | | |

| YEAR | SHIP | GRT | BLDR | YARD No. | OFF. No. | NHP | IHP | TYPE | ENG. No. | REMARKS |
|---|---|---|---|---|---|---|---|---|---|---|
| 1885 | Fernlands | 2148 | WG | 306 | 92905 | 203 | - | T3Cy. | 2 | LR(87) 170NHP:l.d. "Roumelia"? |
| 1885 | Cleveland | 2153 | WG | 308 | 89719 | 200 | - | T3Cy. | 4 | |
| 1885 | Enfield | 2158 | WG | 301 | 92902 | 200 | - | T3Cy. | 1 | 1st Engine from CMEW |
| 1885 | Coot / Stefano Dandria | 1961 | WG | 307 | 92004 | 160 | - | T3Cy. | 3 | |
| 1886 | Wapping | 688 | WG | 312 | 91919 | 120 | - | C2Cy. | 6 | Mudd's patent 'Dynamic valves' |
| 1886 | Poplar | 688 | WG | 313 | 91925 | 150 | - | C2Cy. | 7 | "Flatiron" New B.1898 |
| 1886 | Abeona | 2152 | WG | 315 | 92906 | 180 | - | T3Cy. | 9 | |
| 1886 | Stepney | 688 | WG | 311 | 91913 | 107 | - | C2Cy. | 5 | Mudd's patent 'Dynamic valves' |
| 1886 | Astraea | 2140 | WG | 316 | 92907 | 220 | 900 | T3Cy. | 10 | |
| 1886 | Bakuin | 1669 | WG | 314 | 91944 | 200 | - | T3Cy. | 8 | Tanker. |
| 1886 | Maryland | 2863 | WG | 317 | 91984 | 300 | - | T3Cy. | 11 | |
| 1887 | Montana | 3026 | WG | 329 | 94344 | 325 | 1600 | T3Cy. | 23 | |
| 1887 | Flambro' | 2224 | WG | 326 | 92918 | 217 | 1050 | T3Cy. | 15 | |
| 1887 | Swansea / Maine | 2809 | WG | 322 | 94303 | 239 | 1400 | T3Cy. | 16 | |
| 1887 | Springfield | 2243 | WG | 324 | 94321 | 240 | 1200 | T3Cy. | 18 | |
| 1887 | Amphitrite | 2256 | EW | 149 | 92919 | 200 | 1000 | T3Cy. | 21 | LR 210 NHP |
| 1887 | Worcester / Tenshin M. | 2908 | WG | 318 | 91059 | 260 | 1500 | T3Cy. | 12 | |
| 1887 | Jenny Otto | 1419 | WR | 101 | 76652 | 150 | 800 | T3Cy. | 17 | Blt.1877. Tripled CMEW '87 |
| 1887 | Suez / Hodeidah | 2087 | MI | 298 | 73633 | 241 | 1000 | Quad. | 19 | Blt. 1876. Quad.CMEW '87 |
| 1887 | Oxford / Washtenaw | 2897 | WG | 319 | 91061 | 292 | 1500 | T3Cy. | 13 | |
| 1887 | Heathfield | 2140 | EW | 148 | 94332 | 210 | 1000 | T3Cy. | 20 | |
| 1887 | Goldsbro' | 2247 | WG | 321 | 92914 | 217 | 1050 | T3Cy. | 14 | |
| 1888 | Humber | 2198 | WG | 349 | 95492 | 250 | 1150 | T3Cy. | 38 | |
| 1888 | Duke of Cornwall | 1764 | WG | 339 | 92237 | 156 | 800 | T3Cy. | 27 | |
| 1888 | Walmer Castle/Valencia | 2459 | BC | n.k. | 65729 | 190 | 1100 | T3Cy. | 42 | Blt.1872. Tripled CMEW. 1888 |
| 1888 | Lowlands | 1789 | WG | 336 | 92925 | 150 | 800 | T3Cy. | 26 | |
| 1888 | Marie | 2059 | WG | 345 | Norway | 169 | 900 | T3Cy. | 34 | |
| 1888 | Era | 2379 | EW | 156 | 95955 | 240 | 1250 | T3Cy. | 31 | |
| 1888 | Muriel | 2398 | WG | 351 | 88906 | 200 | 1100 | T3Cy. | 41 | |
| 1888 | Urania | 2591 | WG | 330 | 92922 | 220 | 1250 | T3Cy. | 24 | |
| 1888 | Missouri | 2845 | WG | 346 | 95524 | 274 | 1500 | T3Cy. | 32 | |
| 1888 | Harrow | 2586 | WG | 332 | 94394 | 220 | 1250 | T3Cy. | 22 | LR 240NHP |
| 1888 | Carrie | 1789 | WG | 342 | 88905 | 156 | 800 | T3Cy. | 29 | |
| 1888 | Kittie | 2183 | WG | 331 | 88904 | 210 | 1100 | T2Cy | 25 | |
| 1888 | Cranford | 2293 | WG | 341 | 95459 | 240 | 1250 | T3Cy. | 30 | |

| YEAR | SHIP | GRT | BLDR | YARD No. | OFF. No. | NHP | IHP | TYPE | ENG. No. | REMARKS |
|---|---|---|---|---|---|---|---|---|---|---|
| 1888 | New Borough /Pensacola | 1795 | WG | 340 | 95878 | 150 | 800 | T3Cy. | 28 | |
| 1888 | Egglestone Abbey | 2401 | WG | 343 | 95164 | 200 | 1150 | T3Cy. | 33 | |
| 1889 | Calliope | 2934 | WG | 365 | 97367 | 240 | 1300 | T3Cy. | 45 | |
| 1889 | Duchess of Cornwall | 1772 | WG | 356 | 95904 | 150 | 900 | T3Cy. | 36 | |
| 1889 | Chinglord | 1821 | WG | 369 | 96639 | 168 | 1000 | T3Cy. | 54 | |
| 1889 | Norsa | 1133 | WG | 375 | 97381 | 180 | 1200 | T3Cy. | 60 | |
| 1889 | Falka | 1525 | WG | 355 | 95890 | 156 | 900 | T3Cy. | 40 | |
| 1889 | Clio | 2697 | WG | 354 | 95784 | 220 | 1300 | T3Cy. | 39 | Blockship 1914. |
| 1889 | Mortlake | 2766 | WG | 359 | 96601 | 250 | 1300 | T3Cy. | 44 | |
| 1889 | Ermanarich | 1595 | WG | 364 | German | 150 | 900 | T3Cy. | 49 | |
| 1889 | Redcar | 1841 | WG | 366 | 89727 | 150 | 900 | T3Cy. | 51 | |
| 1889 | Empress / Ningoote | 1380 | WG | 360 | 97362 | 274 | 1850 | T3Cy. | 50 | |
| 1889 | Thurston | 1863 | WG | 358 | 95894 | 169 | 1000 | T3Cy. | 35 | |
| 1889 | Alarich | 1598 | WG | 363 | German | 140 | 900 | T3Cy. | 48 | |
| 1889 | Geiserich/Karthago | 1476 | WG | 362 | German | 156 | 900 | T3Cy. | 47 | |
| 1889 | Romulus | 2739 | WG | 372 | Germany | 250 | 1300 | T3Cy. | 57 | |
| 1889 | Marmion | 1725 | WG | 370 | 97372 | 160 | 1000 | T3Cy. | 56 | |
| 1889 | Reggio | 1218 | IR | 65 | 91369 | 96 | 590 | T3Cy. | 55 | 9k on 6+ T: 1620DWT |
| 1889 | Cornubia | 1750 | WG | 377 | 95905 | 156 | 900 | T3Cy. | 62 | |
| 1889 | Elmville | 1967 | WG | 367 | 95295 | 169 | 1000 | T3Cy. | 52 | |
| 1889 | Eton | 2688 | WG | 380 | 98031 | 240 | 1300 | T3Cy. | 64 | |
| 1889 | Theodorich | 1595 | WG | 361 | Germany | 140 | 900 | T3Cy. | 46 | LR 200NHP |
| 1889 | Garlands | 1987 | WG | 368 | 97363 | 165 | 1000 | T3Cy. | 53 | |
| 1889 | Ariel / Samara | 2884 | WG | 352 | 95892 | 240 | 1300 | T3Cy. | 43 | |
| 1889 | Remus | 2635 | WG | 373 | Germany | 260 | 1300 | T3Cy. | 58 | |
| 1889 | Iona | 2094 | WG | 374 | 97376 | 180 | 1200 | T3Cy. | 59 | 9 K on 11+ T: 3100DWT |
| 1889 | Norlands / Pena Rocias | 1697 | WG | 353 | 95896 | 156 | 900 | T3Cy. | 37 | Still in service 1961. |
| 1889 | John Bright | 2715 | WG | 378 | 96695 | 250 | 1300 | T3Cy. | 63 | |
| 1889 | Westbrook | 1681 | WG | 376 | 96547 | 150 | 900 | T3Cy. | 61 | |
| 1890 | Halifax City / Kestor | 2289 | WG | 391 | 102710 | 200 | 1200 | T3Cy. | 72 | |
| 1890 | Bussorah/Greatham | 2358 | WG | 382 | 97390 | 210 | 1200 | T3Cy. | 66 | |
| 1890 | Fulham | 2069 | WG | 386 | 98087 | 165 | 1000 | T3Cy. | 74 | |
| 1890 | Guernsey | 2856 | WG | 404 | 88909 | 220 | 1300 | T3Cy. | 92 | |
| 1890 | Herman Wedel Jarlsberg | 3023 | WG | 400 | Norway | 240 | 1500 | T3Cy. | 86 | LR 260NHP |
| 1890 | Armenia | 2330 | WG | 381 | 97386 | 200 | 1250 | T3Cy. | 68 | |

| YEAR | SHIP | GRT | BLDR | YARD No. | OFF. No. | NHP | IHP | TYPE | ENG. No. | REMARKS |
|------|------|-----|------|----------|----------|-----|-----|------|----------|---------|
| 1890 | Macduff | 2905 | WG | 403 | 95228 | 288 | 1300 | T3Cy. | 90 | 4300 DWT 10 knots |
| 1890 | Pocklington | 1390 | WG | 383 | 97388 | 130 | 800 | T3Cy. | 69 | |
| 1890 | Sestao | 1447 | WG | 395 | Spain | 150 | 1000 | T3Cy. | 79 | |
| 1890 | Tetartos | 2411 | FS | 47 | Germany | 234 | - | T3Cy. | 78 | Blt. 1883. New E&B CMEW '90 |
| 1890 | Norna | 2242 | EW | 172 | 97397 | 200 | 1200 | T3Cy. | 81 | |
| 1890 | Kingsland | 2016 | WG | 387 | 98126 | 200 | 1000 | T3Cy. | 75 | |
| 1890 | Oaklands | 1719 | WG | 402 | 98496 | 168 | 1000 | T3Cy. | 89 | |
| 1890 | Coatham | 1771 | WG | 398 | 89730 | 150 | 900 | T3Cy. | 84 | |
| 1890 | Frieda | 2072 | WG | 401 | 98498 | 207 | 1200 | T3Cy. | 88 | |
| 1890 | Ipsden | 1748 | WG | 397 | 98493 | 150 | 900 | T3Cy. | 83 | |
| 1890 | Lizzie Cory | 1241 | IR | 67 ? | 97389 | 111 | 700 | T3Cy. | n.k. | |
| 1890 | Calcutta City / Langoe | 2306 | WG | 390 | 96219 | 204 | 1200 | T3Cy. | 91 | |
| 1890 | Malvern | 2493 | WG | 393 | 98115 | 250 | 1300 | T3Cy. | 73 | |
| 1890 | Rangatira | 4045 | WG | 392 | 97216 | 450 | 2180 | T3Cy. | 70 | 10K on 21T  6220DWT |
| 1890 | Zanzibar | 2964 | EW | 178 | 98192 | 300 | 1500 | T3Cy. | 71 ? | |
| 1890 | Bushmills | 2466 | EW | 174 | 96266 | 217 | 1300 | T3Cy. | 87 | |
| 1890 | Umhloti | 2173 | WG | 399 | 98168 | 250 | 1300 | T3Cy. | 85 | |
| 1890 | Umbilo | 1923 | WG | 379 | 98050 | 210 | 1250 | T3Cy. | 65 | LR(00) 232NHP |
| 1890 | Elloe / Konstantinos | 1774 | WG | 396 | 96228 | 147 | 900 | T3Cy. | 82 | |
| 1890 | Manchester | 2049 | WG | 388 | 95199 | 207 | 1200 | T3Cy. | 76 | |
| 1890 | Tekoa | 4050 | WG | 394 | 97473 | 450 | 2180 | T3Cy. | 80 | 6220 DWT  10k on 21T. LR412NHP |
| 1890 | Taurus | 2165 | WG | 406 | Norway | 180 | 1200 | T3Cy. | 77 | |
| 1891 | Gledhow | 2661 | WG | 409 | 98913 | 239 | 1300 | T3Cy. | 97 | |
| 1891 | Hupeh | 2819 | WG | 428 | 99024 | 240 | 1300 | T3Cy. | 118 | |
| 1891 | City of Worcester | 2404 | OG | 89 | 98506 | | 1200 | T3Cy. | 105 | Sunk 4/12/1899: see "Norburn" |
| 1891 | Bramham | 1978 | WG | 389 | 98912 | 160 | 1000 | T3Cy. | 94 | |
| 1891 | Jessie | 2256 | WG | 425 | 88910 | 190 | 1200 | T3Cy. | 115 | |
| 1891 | Ruabon | 2004 | WG | 427 | 98417 | 160 | 1000 | T3Cy. | 117 | LR 188 NHP |
| 1891 | Harold | 1734 | WG | 411 | 98510 | 168 | 1000 | T3Cy. | 100 | |
| 1891 | Castleton | 2395 | WG | 421 | 98772 | 190 | 1200 | T3Cy. | 111 | |
| 1891 | Inchbarra / Telesfora | 4069 | WG | 419 | 99305 | 500 | 2000 | T3Cy. | 109 | |
| 1891 | Saint Andrews | 3066 | WG | 423 | Norway | 250 | 1300 | T3Cy. | 113 | |
| 1891 | Westow | 2283 | WG | 424 | 99491 | 200 | 1200 | T3Cy. | 114 | |
| 1891 | Silvia/K.Arthur/Gyptis | 1229 | IR | 72 | 99172 | 109 | 700 | T3Cy. | 106 | |
| 1891 | Mab | 2838 | WG | 422 | 97977 | 220 | 1200 | T3Cy. | 112 | |

| YEAR | SHIP | GRT | BLDR | YARD No. | OFF. No. | NHP | IHP | TYPE | ENG. No. | REMARKS |
|------|------|-----|------|----------|----------|-----|-----|------|----------|---------|
| 1891 | Rhio | 1402 | WG | 418 | 98873 | 120 | 800 | T3Cy. | 108 | Wrecked Ushant 6/1894 |
| 1891 | Blenheim | 2403 | WG | 408 | 96559 | 215 | 1205 | T3Cy. | 96 | |
| 1891 | Lesbury | 2623 | WG | 413 | 98931 | 240 | 1300 | T3Cy. | 99 | |
| 1891 | Lincolnshire | 2682 | WG | 410 | 98507 | 240 | 1300 | T3Cy. | 98 | |
| 1891 | Rothesay | 2007 | WG | 414 | 98412 | 160 | 1000 | T3Cy. | 102 | |
| 1891 | Buckingham | 2879 | WG | 407 | 98608 | 240 | 1500 | T3Cy. | 95 | Hull only cost £22,500. |
| 1891 | General Boyd | 1354 | WG | 415 | 95145 | 217 | 900 | C2Cy. | 103 | LR 157 NHP |
| 1891 | Holmlea | 1781 | WG | 417 | 98513 | 150 | 900 | T3Cy. | 107 | |
| 1891 | Heighington | 2800 | WG | 405 | 98502 | 239 | 1300 | T3Cy. | 93 | |
| 1891 | Adelphi Chrissoveloni | 2332 | WG | 416 | Greece | 200 | 1250 | T3Cy. | 104 | |
| 1891 | Hardanger | 2419 | WG | 420 | 98515 | 215 | 1250 | T3Cy. | 110 | |
| 1891 | Shantung | 2820 | WG | 429 | 99039 | 240 | 1300 | T3Cy. | 119 | |
| 1891 | Elmete | 1991 | WG | 412 | 98930 | 160 | 1000 | T3Cy. | 101 | Wrecked 2/1895 |
| 1891 | Ariadne | 1988 | WG | 426 | 98989 | 160 | 1000 | T3Cy. | 116 | |
| 1891 | Ramillies | 2935 | WG | 445 | 98425 | 250 | 1550 | T3Cy. | 137 | |
| 1892 | Melbourne | 1739 | WG | 435 | 98524 | 162 | 900 | T3Cy. | 125 | |
| 1892 | Thyra | 3406 | WG | 432 | 98523 | 240 | 1500 | T3Cy. | 122 | |
| 1892 | Mashona | 2735 | WG | 437 | 99053 | 500 | 2000 | T3Cy. | 127 | LR(00) 279NHP ? |
| 1892 | Saint Giles | 3372 | WG | 447 | 102071 | 277 | 1600 | T3Cy. | 139 | i.d. as "Mendip" ? |
| 1892 | Tudor | 1113 | IR | 78 | 99414 | 140 | 900 | T3Cy. | 136 | |
| 1892 | Nina Mendl | 2415 | WG | 440 | 99077 | 250 | 1300 | T3Cy. | 131 | |
| 1892 | Aldworth | 3369 | WG | 455 | 98540 | 279 | 1600 | T3Cy. | 147 | |
| 1892 | Conch | 3555 | WG | 448 | 101953 | 324 | 2000 | T3Cy. | 140 | Tanker |
| 1892 | Masonic | 2399 | WG | 433 | 99138 | 220 | 1800 | T3Cy. | 123 | LR 239NHp |
| 1892 | Murex | 3564 | WG | 442 | 101899 | 324 | 2000 | T3Cy. | 130 | Tanker. LR(00) 324NHP |
| 1892 | Escholbrook | 2143 | WG | 446 | 99143 | 207 | 1200 | T3Cy. | 135 | |
| 1892 | Argyll | 2953 | WG | 439 | 99232 | 283 | 1300 | T3Cy. | 129 | Scrapped 1962 ("San Luciano") |
| 1892 | Blagdon | 1993 | WG | 454 | 101961 | 140 | 1000 | T3Cy. | 146 | |
| 1892 | Quantock/Florence Pile | 3358 | WG | 441 | 101934 | 279 | 1600 | T3Cy. | 134 | |
| 1892 | Manica | 2733 | WG | 438 | 99067 | 500 | 2000 | T3Cy. | 128 | Trialtrip Sunday 8.5.92 |
| 1892 | Spheroid | 1941 | WG | 430 | 99026 | 220 | 1300 | T3Cy. | 120 | |
| 1892 | James Tucker | 2560 | WG | 458 | 98430 | 220 | 1300 | T3Cy. | 151 | |
| 1892 | Arapahoe / Inchmaree | 4763 | WG | 444 | 102052 | 500 | 2600 | T3Cy. | 133 | LR 266 NHP |
| 1892 | Buckminster | 2035 | WG | 453 | 101943 | 175 | 1000 | T3Cy. | 145 | |
| 1892 | Mount Stewart | 739 | WG | 431 | 99602 | 120 | 800 | T3Cy. | 121 | |

| YEAR | SHIP | GRT | BLDR | YARD No. | OFF. No. | NHP | IHP | TYPE | ENG. No. | REMARKS |
|------|------|-----|------|----------|----------|-----|-----|------|----------|---------|
| 1892 | Venus | 1223 | WG | 436 | Germany | 113 | 700 | T3Cy. | 126 | |
| 1892 | Alberta / Inchulva | 4823 | WG | 443 | 99439 | 500 | 2250 | T3Cy. | 132 | LR 381 NHP |
| 1892 | Milo | 1754 | WG | 434 | 99492 | 156 | 900 | T3Cy. | 124 | |
| 1892 | Grafíoe | 2996 | FW | 195 | 99681 | 239 | 1300 | T3Cy. | 138 | |
| 1892 | Hildawell | 1919 | WG | 452 | 98530 | 224 | 1250 | T3Cy. | 144 | |
| 1893 | Pacific | 2622 | WG | 469 | 102932 | 224 | 1500 | T3Cy. | 163 | |
| 1893 | Penarth | 3109 | WG | 463 | 98432 | 290 | 1500 | T3Cy. | 155 | Wrecked Bosphorus 2/1894 |
| 1893 | Mark Lane | 2095 | PAL | 379 | 79659 | 212 | 1000 | C2Cy. | none | Eng. Conv.1893. NB '93. Blt'78 |
| 1893 | Nador | 2031 | WG | 460 | 98537 | 167 | 1000 | T3Cy. | 153 | |
| 1893 | Elax | 4015 | WG | 450 | 102764 | 357 | 2250 | T3Cy. | 143 | Tanker. |
| 1893 | Baracaldo | 1093 | WG | 467 | Spain | 127 | 700 | T3Cy. | 160 | |
| 1893 | Adjutant | 2393 | WG | 461 | 102776 | 240 | 1250 | T3Cy. | 152 | LR 225NHP |
| 1893 | Ariadne Alexandra | 1986 | WG | 466 | 102779 | 175 | 1000 | T3Cy. | 159 | |
| 1893 | David Mainland | 1898 | WG | 468 | 99493 | 156 | 900 | T3Cy. | 161 | |
| 1893 | Maori | 5317 | SH | 184 | 104031 | 461 | 2750 | T3Cy. | 158 | |
| 1893 | Bullmouth | 4018 | WG | 465 | 102805 | 357 | 2250 | T3Cy. | 157 | Tanker. |
| 1893 | Indralema / Bray Head | 3150 | SH | 187 | 102133 | 264 | - | T3Cy. | 164 | |
| 1893 | Sweden | 569 | JL | n.k. | 63031 | 80 | | C2Cy. | none | Conv. & NB '93: sunk '93 |
| 1893 | Twilight | 1919 | FW | 202 | 102711 | 169 | 1000 | T3Cy. | 165 | |
| 1893 | Burma | 3078 | WG | 456 | Aust-Hung | 256 | 1200 | T3Cy. | 142 | |
| 1893 | Chickahominy | 2875 | FW | 200 | 102706 | 401 | 2400 | T3Cy. | 156 | |
| 1893 | Oscar II | 3060 | WG | 457 | Norway | 220 | 1300 | T3Cy. | 149 | Trunkdeck. 9k on 14T 4663DWT |
| 1893 | Castanos | 2958 | WG | 471 | 98438 | 258 | 1500 | T3Cy. | 167 | |
| 1893 | Albania | 1212 | WG | 273 | 86961 | 188 | | C2Cy. | none | Conv. & NB '93. |
| 1893 | Repton | 2881 | SH | 191 | 102838 | 245 | 1300 | T3Cy. | 168 | Laid down as "Unionist" |
| 1893 | Roumania / Algorteno | 2413 | WG | 462 | Spain | 239 | 1300 | T3Cy. | 154 | |
| 1893 | Aeolus | 2875 | SH | 188 | 102708 | 245 | 1300 | T3Cy. | 162 | |
| 1893 | Webster | 3101 | WG | 459 | 98539 | 270 | 1500 | T3Cy. | 150 | LR 256NHP |
| 1893 | Clam | 3552 | WG | 449 | 101973 | 299 | 2000 | T3Cy. | 141 | Tanker |
| 1893 | Volute | 4500 | WG | 451 | 102789 | 399 | 2250 | T3Cy. | 148 | Tanker. |
| 1894 | Gardepee | 1126 | PIC | 57 | 86487 | 191 | - | Comp. | none | Built 1882: Conv. 1894 |
| 1894 | Ribston | 3372 | WG | 472 | 102837 | 260 | - | T3Cy. | 169 | |
| 1894 | Strathord | 4040 | WG | 482 | 104553 | 404 | 1600 | T3Cy. | 180 | I.d. as "Peruvia" |
| 1894 | Lady Gray | 2545 | WG | 479 | 99494 | 224 | 1200 | T3Cy. | 176 | I.d. as "Claudio" |
| 1894 | South Gwalia / Povena | 2116 | WG | 478 | 98445 | 188 | - | T3Cy. | 172 | |

| YEAR | SHIP | GRT | BLDR | YARD No. | OFF. No. | NHP | IHP | TYPE | ENG. No. | REMARKS |
|---|---|---|---|---|---|---|---|---|---|---|
| 1894 | Garton | 2734 | WG | 477 | 102941 | 239 | - | T3Cy. | 174 | |
| 1894 | Chatburn | 1942 | WG | 474 | 102713 | 169 | - | T3Cy. | 166 | |
| 1894 | Stuart | 1212 | IR | 91 | 102147 | 140 | - | T3Cy. | n.k. | |
| 1894 | Coniscliffe/Urquiola | 2547 | WG | 476 | 102716 | 224 | - | T3Cy. | 175 | Laid down as "Mar Cantabrico" |
| 1894 | Strathnairn | 4038 | WG | 480 | 102690 | 404 | - | T3Cy. | 171 | |
| 1894 | Strathfillan | 4046 | WG | 486 | 104590 | 404 | 1600 | T3Cy. | 181 | l.d. as "Montauk" |
| 1894 | Emmanuel / Graphic | 2490 | WG | 485 | 105015 | 239 | - | T3Cy. | 183 | |
| 1894 | Rounton | 2650 | WG | 473 | 102845 | 239 | - | T3Cy. | 173 | |
| 1894 | Strathness / Buceros | 4035 | WG | 475 | 102672 | 404 | - | T3Cy. | 170 | |
| 1894 | Giustizia | | ? | n.k. | — | | 700 | T3Cy. | 178 | |
| 1894 | Larch [Iron] | 1370 | JB | 51 | 68987 | 150 | | Comp. | none | Blt. 1878: Conv. & NB TR 1894 |
| 1894 | Severus | 3409 | WG | 483 | Norway | 295 | 1200 | T3Cy. | 179 | |
| 1894 | Bayvoe / Wenvoe | 2969 | WG | 481 | 98442 | 258 | 1200 | T3Cy. | 177 | |
| 1894 | Bainbridge | 1900 | WG | 484 | 102722 | 140 | - | T3Cy. | 182 | |
| 1895 | Arion | 2838 | FW | 211 | 102731 | 239 | 1250 | T3Cy. | 188 | l.d. as "Theodoros Pangalos" |
| 1895 | Penarth | 3035 | WG | 508 | 105177 | 266 | 1200 | T3Cy. | 508 | |
| 1895 | Holgate | 2604 | WG | 511 | 105783 | 244 | 1100 | T3Cy. | 511 | |
| 1895 | Middleton | 2506 | WG | 496 | 105046 | 239 | 1100 | T3Cy. | 195 | |
| 1895 | Pectan | 4778 | WG | 498 | 105735 | 398 | 1700 | T3Cy. | 197 | Tanker. LR 581NHP |
| 1895 | Baluchistan | 2409 | WG | 510 | 104951 | 224 | 1000 | T3Cy. | 510 | l.d. as "Tom"/"Ardia" |
| 1895 | Haslingden | 1934 | WG | 490 | 102725 | 169 | 750 | T3Cy. | 187 | |
| 1895 | Parklands / Ameland | 2520 | WG | 494 | 102730 | 239 | 1100 | T3Cy. | 193 | l.d. as "Hocking" |
| 1895 | Majestic | 2586 | WG | 500 | 105050 | 239 | 1100 | T3Cy. | 199 | l.d. as "Bartolo" |
| 1895 | Martin | 1904 | WG | 487 | 99495 | 156 | 700 | T3Cy. | 184 | |
| 1895 | Lady Olivia/Kirkstall | 1831 | WG | 505 | 102735 | 156 | 700 | T3Cy. | 505 | L. as "Baron Gardien" |
| 1895 | Telena | 4778 | WG | 499 | 105764 | 398 | 1700 | T3Cy. | 198 | Tanker. |
| 1895 | Mathilda | 3480 | WG | 497 | Norway | 260 | 1200 | T3Cy. | 196 | |
| 1895 | Lesreaulx | 3009 | WG | 488 | 105171 | 258 | 1200 | T3Cy. | 185 | |
| 1895 | Argo | 3070 | WG | 501 | 102733 | 271 | 1200 | T3Cy. | 501 | |
| 1895 | Ellie | 1927 | WG | 495 | 99496 | 156 | 700 | T3Cy. | 194 | |
| 1895 | Bertholey | 2278 | WG | 509 | 105178 | 223 | 1000 | T3Cy. | 509 | l.d. as "Eleonara Maersk" |
| 1895 | Romsdalen | 2548 | WG | 493 | 102729 | 224 | 1000 | T3Cy. | 192 | Laid down as "Rizkori Mendi" |
| 1895 | Aotea / Naneric | 6364 | SH | 199 | 104047 | 602 | 2100 | T3Cy. | 190 | |
| 1895 | Clermiston / Rocio | 1282 | WG | 491 | 98883 | 127 | 600 | T3Cy. | 189 | |
| 1895 | Rossall | 2739 | WG | 492 | 104848 | 225 | 1100 | T3Cy. | 191 | |

| YEAR | SHIP | GRT | BLDR | YARD No. | OFF. No. | NHP | IHP | TYPE | ENG. No. | REMARKS |
|------|------|-----|------|----------|----------|-----|-----|------|----------|---------|
| 1895 | Maling | 3075 | WG | 489 | 102724 | 241 | 1200 | T3Cy. | 186 | I.d. as "Durango" |
| 1895 | Marie Elsie | 2606 | WG | 504 | 105756 | 247 | 1100 | T3Cy. | 504 | |
| 1895 | Saint Ronald | 3079 | WG | 503 | 105346 | 218 | 1200 | T3Cy. | 503 | I.d. as "Portmanock" |
| 1895 | Firby | 2417 | WG | 506 | 99497 | 224 | 1000 | T3Cy. | 506 | I.d. as "Voss" |
| 1895 | Scandinavien | 1338 | WG | 172 | Norway | - | 1050 | T3Cy. | none | Convtd '95. ex"Yarm"(WG:1877) |
| 1895 | Nanette | 2142 | WG | 507 | 102739 | 224 | 1000 | T3Cy. | 507 | I.d. as "Gloria" |
| 1895 | Aries | 3071 | WG | 502 | 102734 | 271 | 1200 | T3Cy. | 502 | |
| 1896 | Cambrian / Bostonian | 5626 | WG | 524 | 106957 | 660 | 4000 | T3Cy. | 524 | 14K. El. light |
| 1896 | Jupiter | 1920 | WG | 519 | Germany | 148 | 900 | T3Cy. | 519 | |
| 1896 | Sigurd | 2126 | WG | 516 | Denmark | 198 | 1100 | T3Cy. | 516 | |
| 1896 | Dalegarth | 1613 | WG | 527 | 106835 | 238 | 1200 | T3Cy. | 527 | |
| 1896 | Margareta / Inchmona | 3484 | WG | 512 | 105382 | 326 | 2200 | Quad. | 512 | 6170DW: 9k on 13+T. 5-crank. |
| 1896 | Mars | 1936 | WG | 523 | Germany | 148 | 800 | T3Cy. | 523 | |
| 1896 | Balderton | 2620 | WG | 522 | 106952 | 244 | 1300 | T3Cy. | 522 | |
| 1896 | Ebani / Loong Sang | 1738 | WG | 515 | 105383 | 245 | 1200 | T3Cy. | 515 | |
| 1896 | Simonside | 3033 | WG | 517 | 106408 | 266 | 1500 | T3Cy. | 517 | |
| 1896 | Atlantic/Brattingsborg | 3095 | WG | 521 | 106708 | 271 | 1300 | T3Cy. | 521 | |
| 1896 | Laristan | 2134 | WG | 526 | 104954 | 218 | 1200 | T3Cy. | 526 | |
| 1896 | Greylands / Ed.Gustave | 2625 | WG | 514 | 102741 | 244 | 1300 | T3Cy. | 514 | "L. as ""Norrkoping""" |
| 1896 | Alete | 3063 | WG | 520 | 109692 | 279 | 1550 | T3Cy. | 520 | |
| 1896 | Gallia | 1862 | WG | 528 | Denmark | 188 | 1000 | T3Cy. | 528 | |
| 1896 | Ragnar | 2100 | WG | 518 | Denmark | 198 | 1000 | T3Cy. | 518 | Laid down as "Sigurd" |
| 1896 | Jomsborg | 1888 | WG | 525 | Denmark | 188 | 1000 | T3Cy. | 525 | |
| 1896 | Taisho Maru / Valhalla | 2628 | WG | 513 | 102742 | 225 | 1250 | T3Cy. | 513 | |
| 1897 | Afghanistan | 2753 | WG | 531 | 104956 | 240 | 1300 | T3Cy. | 531 | |
| 1897 | Arlington | 3092 | WG | 537 | 106742 | 260 | 1500 | T3Cy. | 537 | sunk 26.7.1917 |
| 1897 | Helga | 1182 | WG | 534 | Denmark | 127 | 800 | T3Cy. | 534 | |
| 1897 | Eveline | 2605 | WG | 536 | 106615 | 244 | 1300 | T3Cy. | 536 | |
| 1897 | Olaf | 1890 | WG | 530 | Denmark | 198 | 1100 | T3Cy. | 530 | |
| 1897 | Martha / Marselisborg | 1182 | WG | 535 | Denmark | 127 | 800 | T3Cy. | 535 | |
| 1897 | Koordistan | 2740 | WG | 548 | 104958 | 239 | 1300 | T3Cy. | 548 | |
| 1897 | Sturton | 2128 | WG | 539 | 106748 | 220 | 1200 | T3Cy. | 539 | |
| 1897 | Vlug | 1150 | WG | 529 | Holland | 127 | 800 | T3Cy. | 529 | |
| 1897 | Atlas | 3090 | WG | 541 | 106964 | 260 | 1500 | T3Cy. | 541 | |
| 1897 | Alpha | 2028 | WG | 545 | Dutch | 165 | 900 | T3Cy. | 545 | |

| YEAR | SHIP | GRT | BLDR | YARD No. | OFF. No. | NHP | IHP | TYPE | ENG. No. | REMARKS |
|---|---|---|---|---|---|---|---|---|---|---|
| 1897 | Manoussis | 2115 | SH | 223 | Greece | 198 | 1100 | T3Cy. | 201 | |
| 1897 | Olivemoor | 3069 | WG | 542 | 108241 | 260 | 1500 | T3Cy. | 542 | |
| 1897 | Britannic / Aldersgate | 3076 | WG | 532 | 106736 | 281 | 1500 | T3Cy. | 532 | |
| 1897 | Sceptre | 2579 | WG | 540 | 106621 | 244 | 1300 | T3Cy. | 540 | |
| 1897 | Pallas | 2052 | WG | 543 | Germany | 156 | 900 | T3Cy. | 543 | |
| 1897 | Jacob Bright | 2848 | IR | 100 | 105676 | 240 | 1100 | T3Cy. | 200 | Laid down as "Ellina" |
| 1897 | Harlingen/Ethelbrytha | 3084 | WG | 547 | 106106 | 295 | 1700 | T3Cy. | 547 | |
| 1897 | Saint Helen | 2599 | WG | 544 | 108250 | 244 | 1200 | T3Cy. | 544 | |
| 1897 | Pendennis | 2123 | WG | 533 | 108015 | 218 | 1200 | T3Cy. | 533 | |
| 1897 | Ambassador | 2578 | WG | 538 | 106618 | 242 | 1300 | T3Cy. | 538 | |
| 1897 | Cresyl | 2342 | WG | 546 | 109007 | 227 | 1250 | T3Cy. | 546 | |
| 1897 | Rex | 1214 | JL | 559 | Sweden | 1800 | 1600 | T3Cy. | 202 | Lost 1900 |
| 1898 | Londesborough | 3071 | WG | 567 | 109085 | 258 | - | T3Cy. | 567 | |
| 1898 | Emanuel | 1779 | WG | 551 | Sweden | 150 | 900 | T3Cy. | 551 | |
| 1898 | Joseph Merryweather | 2144 | WG | 559 | 106986 | 220 | 1200 | T3Cy. | 559 | |
| 1898 | Cardiff | 2808 | WG | 554 | 105197 | 255 | 1300 | T3Cy. | 554 | |
| 1898 | Miles Coverdale | 2308 | WG | 570 | 109721 | 223 | 1200 | T3Cy. | 570 | |
| 1898 | Mountby | 3015 | WG | 569 | 106994 | 256 | 1500 | T3Cy. | 569 | |
| 1898 | Sanna | 3393 | WG | 550 | Norway | 292 | 1500 | T3Cy. | 550 | |
| 1898 | Marie Suzanne | 3106 | WG | 558 | 109952 | 292 | 1500 | T3Cy. | 558 | |
| 1898 | Non-marine | | | | | | 2000 | T3Cy. | 226 | London Electric Power Co. |
| 1898 | Povena | 2104 | WG | 553 | Spain | 206 | 1200 | T3Cy. | 553 | |
| 1898 | Wilster | 2101 | WG | 556 | 106985 | 223 | 1200 | T3Cy. | 556 | |
| 1898 | not known | | ? | n.k. | France ? | | 700 | T3Cy. | 227 | CASTINGS SENT TO FRANCE. |
| 1898 | Mount Royal/Br. Maple | 8747 | SH | 230 | 109498 | 608 | 3600 | T3Cy. | 204 | |
| 1898 | L.H.Carl | 1916 | WG | 563 | Denmark | 196 | - | T3Cy. | 563 | |
| 1898 | Ran | 3036 | WG | 571 | Norway | 280 | 1500 | T3Cy. | 571 | |
| 1898 | Araxes / Marselisborg | 2760 | WG | 555 | Denmark | 246 | 1300 | T3Cy. | 555 | |
| 1898 | Ceres | 2009 | WG | 562 | Germany | 154 | 900 | T3Cy. | 562 | |
| 1898 | Chicago / Etonian | 6438 | FW | 232 | 109069 | 842 | 5500 | T3Cy. | 203 | Twin screw. Torpedoed 3/1918 |
| 1898 | Kronborg | 3225 | WG | 572 | Denmark | 292 | 1700 | T3Cy. | 572 | |
| 1898 | Goolistan | 2746 | WG | 549 | 104960 | 240 | 1300 | T3Cy. | 549 | |
| 1898 | Pendeen | 2124 | WG | 575 | 109218 | 217 | 1300 | T3Cy. | 575 | |
| 1898 | Bergenhus | 2606 | IR | 105 | Norway | 295 | 1500 | T3Cy. | 205 | |
| 1898 | Mancunia | 3533 | WG | 564 | 108834 | 322 | 2000 | T3Cy. | 564 | |

| YEAR | SHIP | GRT | BLDR | YARD No. | OFF. No. | NHP | IHP | TYPE | ENG. No. | REMARKS |
|---|---|---|---|---|---|---|---|---|---|---|
| 1898 | Easingwold | 3167 | WG | 560 | 109970 | 292 | 1500 | T3Cy. | 560 | |
| 1898 | Azul | 3074 | WG | 557 | 108385 | 296 | 1500 | T3Cy. | 557 | |
| 1898 | Algorta | 2120 | WG | 552 | Spain | 208 | 1200 | T3Cy. | 552 | |
| 1898 | Everest | 2109 | WG | 565 | 106991 | 217 | 1200 | T3Cy. | 565 | |
| 1898 | Turkistan | 3240 | WG | 566 | 109643 | 460 | 2550 | T3Cy. | 566 | |
| 1899 | Penmount | 2324 | WG | 602 | 109221 | 218 | 1250 | T3Cy. | 602 | |
| 1899 | Harriet | 1392 | WG | 596 | Denmark | 126 | 800 | T3Cy. | 596 | |
| 1899 | Elantsobe | 2398 | WG | 580 | Spain | 246 | 1300 | T3Cy. | 580 | |
| 1899 | Alderney | 3090 | WG | 587 | Norway | 280 | 1500 | T3Cy. | 587 | |
| 1899 | John Coverdale | 3014 | WG | 581 | 109723 | 280 | 1500 | T3Cy. | 581 | |
| 1899 | Airedale | 3044 | WG | 578 | 110105 | 293 | 1500 | T3Cy. | 578 | |
| 1899 | Parana | 3034 | WG | 584 | 109784 | 280 | 1500 | T3Cy. | 584 | LR 258NHP |
| 1899 | Elswick Park | 3403 | WG | 586 | 110338 | 271 | 1700 | T3Cy. | 586 | |
| 1899 | Helsingborg | 2297 | WG | 600 | Sweden | 221 | 1250 | T3Cy. | 600 | |
| 1899 | Glenroy | 2754 | WG | 590 | 112403 | 245 | 1300 | T3Cy. | 590 | |
| 1899 | Inchkeith | 3757 | WG | 583 | 110590 | 310 | 2000 | Quad. | 583 | LR 266 NHP: 5-crank. |
| 1899 | Kumara | 6034 | SH | 245 | 110258 | 691 | 3500 | T3Cy. | 206 | |
| 1899 | Claudius | 3520 | WG | 577 | Germany | 300 | 2000 | T3Cy. | 577 | |
| 1899 | Mundaka | 2396 | WG | 579 | Spain | 217 | 1300 | T3Cy. | 579 | |
| 1899 | Bardistan / Lysaker | 2034 | WG | 574 | n.k. | 206 | - | T3Cy. | 574 | By 1900 'Lysaker', Norway. |
| 1899 | Raithwaite | 3029 | WG | 576 | 106995 | 294 | 1500 | T3Cy. | 576 | |
| 1899 | Kilnsea | 3122 | WG | 595 | 110751 | 264 | 1500 | T3Cy. | 595 | |
| 1899 | Wearside | 3560 | WG | 594 | 109704 | 298 | 2000 | T3Cy. | 594 | |
| 1899 | Darleydale | 3095 | WG | 593 | 112407 | 280 | 1500 | T3Cy. | 593 | |
| 1899 | Ras Mora | 3345 | WG | 582 | 110134 | 292 | 1700 | T3Cy. | 582 | LR(00) 276NHP |
| 1899 | Northlands | 2775 | WG | 597 | 109790 | 250 | 1300 | T3Cy. | 597 | |
| 1899 | Beta | 1983 | WG | 588 | Holland | 154 | 900 | T3Cy. | 588 | |
| 1899 | Shirley | 3403 | WG | 604 | 112668 | 292 | 1700 | T3Cy. | 604 | |
| 1899 | Rowena | 3016 | WG | 589 | 112401 | 280 | 1500 | T3Cy. | 589 | LR(00) 258NHP |
| 1899 | Craigleith | 3402 | WG | 573 | 109592 | 292 | - | T3Cy. | 573 | |
| 1899 | Olanda | 2164 | WG | 591 | Holland | 223 | 1200 | T3Cy. | 591 | |
| 1899 | Mavisbrook | 2134 | WG | 585 | 111208 | 217 | 1200 | T3Cy. | 585 | |
| 1899 | Sheppy Allison | 2301 | WG | 592 | 112408 | 223 | 1250 | T3Cy. | 592 | |
| 1899 | Nubia | 3622 | WG | 599 | Germany | 310 | 2000 | T3Cy. | 599 | |
| 1899 | Sandsend | 3814 | WG | 598 | 112413 | 321 | 2000 | T3Cy. | 598 | sunk 16.8.1917 |

| YEAR | SHIP | GRT | BLDR | YARD No. | OFF. No. | NHP | IHP | TYPE | ENG. No. | REMARKS |
|---|---|---|---|---|---|---|---|---|---|---|
| 1900 | Denaby | 2987 | WG | 606 | 110790 | 274 | 1500 | T3Cy. | 606 | |
| 1900 | Llansannor | 3568 | WG | 605 | 109798 | 322 | 2000 | T3Cy. | 605 | |
| 1900 | Dulcie | 2032 | WG | 607 | 109726 | 200 | 1200 | T3Cy. | 607 | |
| 1900 | Loppersum | 2023 | WG | 615 | Holland | 153 | 900 | T3Cy. | 615 | |
| 1900 | Louise Roth /Winnfield | 3434 | WG | 626 | 109711 | 280 | 2000 | T3Cy. | 626 | |
| 1900 | Numidia | 3382 | WG | 610 | Germany | 260 | 1500 | T3Cy. | 610 | NHP from LR(04) |
| 1900 | Gorjistan | 3261 | WG | 613 | 109649 | 457 | 2550 | T3Cy. | 613 | LR(04) 262NHP |
| 1900 | Membland | 3026 | WG | 617 | 112422 | 280 | 1500 | T3Cy. | 617 | |
| 1900 | Coniston | 3544 | WG | 621 | 112429 | 321 | 2000 | T3Cy. | 621 | |
| 1900 | Inchmario / Rhenania | 4201 | WG | 616 | 113418 | 299 | 2000 | Quad. | 616 | 5-crank. |
| 1900 | Kenley | 3771 | WG | 609 | 112727 | 322 | 2000 | T3Cy. | 609 | LR(04) 297NHP |
| 1900 | Westminster Bridge | 3667 | WG | 619 | 112774 | 268 | 1700 | T3Cy. | 619 | |
| 1900 | Ootmarsum | 2343 | WG | 611 | Holland | 153 | 1100 | T3Cy. | 611 | |
| 1900 | Toronto | 6035 | WG | 603 | 113569 | 660 | 5600 | 2T3Cy | 603 | Twin Screw.LR(04) 776NHP |
| 1900 | Yarborough | 3134 | WG | 612 | 113572 | 267 | 1500 | T3Cy. | 612 | |
| 1900 | Gamma | 2198 | WG | 625 | Holland | 165 | 1000 | T3Cy. | 625 | |
| 1900 | Inchdune | 4199 | WG | 614 | 113412 | 299 | 2000 | Quad. | 614 | 5-crank. |
| 1900 | Tabaristan / Inkonka | 3430 | WG | 620 | 109650 | 484 | 2000 | T3Cy. | 620 | |
| 1900 | Armanistan/Zanos Silne | 2237 | WG | 627 | 113762 | 222 | 1250 | T3Cy. | 627 | later Greek Flag. |
| 1900 | Skipsea | 2993 | WG | 601 | 110776 | 280 | 1500 | T3Cy. | 601 | |
| 1900 | Grayfield | 2120 | WG | 608 | 112707 | 215 | 1100 | T3Cy. | 608 | |
| 1900 | Knud II | 1944 | WG | 618 | Denmark | 194 | 1100 | T3Cy. | 618 | |
| 1900 | La Loire | 5554 | CF | n.k. | France | - | 4000 | 2T3Cy | 207 | CASTINGS & FORGINGS. Twin Sc. |
| 1900 | Nassovia | 3902 | WG | 623 | Germany | 274 | 2000 | Quad. | 623 | 5-crank. |
| 1900 | Erik II | 1943 | WG | 622 | Denmark | 194 | 1100 | T3Cy. | 622 | |
| 1901 | Battersea Bridge | 3360 | WG | 646 | 114781 | 294 | 1700 | T3Cy. | 646 | LR(04) 268NHP |
| 1901 | Westfield | 3418 | WG | 628 | 112834 | 268 | 1700 | T3Cy. | 628 | |
| 1901 | Atheniana | 2300 | WG | 650 | 115128 | 225 | 1250 | T3Cy. | 650 | i.d. as 'Barmouth' |
| 1901 | Dalarne / Moldavia | 2320 | WG | 644 | Sweden | 194 | 1200 | T3Cy. | 644 | |
| 1901 | Numantia | 4503 | WG | 633 | Germany | 369 | 2300 | T3Cy. | 633 | |
| 1901 | Oakley | 3958 | WG | 638 | 113511 | 297 | 2000 | T3Cy. | 638 | |
| 1901 | Etonian | 3850 | WG | 630 | 85276 | 360 | 2000 | T3Cy. | 630 | LR(04) 297NHP |
| 1901 | Sarmatia | 2350 | WG | 631 | Denmark | 221 | 1250 | T3Cy. | 631 | |
| 1901 | Putney Bridge | 3328 | WG | 651 | 114803 | 269 | 2000 | T3Cy. | 651 | |
| 1901 | Dunholme | 3313 | WG | 636 | 112441 | 300 | 2000 | T3Cy. | 636 | LR(06) 319NHP |

| YEAR | SHIP | GRT | BLDR | YARD No. | OFF. No. | NHP | IHP | TYPE | ENG. No. | REMARKS |
|---|---|---|---|---|---|---|---|---|---|---|
| 1901 | Merchiston | 1839 | WG | 648 | 115121 | 156 | 1000 | T3Cy. | 648 | |
| 1901 | Marie Z. Michalinos | 3051 | WG | 649 | Greece | 300 | 1700 | T3Cy. | 649 | |
| 1901 | Euterpe | 3540 | RD | 483 | 114762 | 318 | 2000 | T3Cy. | 208 | |
| 1901 | Knias Gortschakow | 3287 | WG | 640 | Russia | 297 | 1700 | T3Cy. | 640 | |
| 1901 | Southlands | 2984 | WG | 642 | 113546 | 269 | 1500 | T3Cy. | 642 | |
| 1901 | Dagny | 1192 | WG | 635 | Denmark | 125 | 800 | T3Cy. | 635 | |
| 1901 | Vauxhall Bridge | 3301 | WG | 629 | 114670 | 268 | 1700 | T3Cy. | 629 | |
| 1901 | Brunhilda | 2296 | WG | 641 | 112443 | 225 | 1250 | T3Cy. | 641 | |
| 1901 | Rosebank | 3836 | WG | 632 | 112438 | 319 | 2000 | T3Cy. | 632 | sunk 31.5.1917 |
| 1901 | Selsdon | 3801 | WG | 637 | 114716 | 297 | 2000 | T3Cy. | 637 | |
| 1901 | Nicomedia | 4498 | WG | 634 | Germany | 369 | 2300 | T3Cy. | 634 | |
| 1901 | Mountfields | 3038 | WG | 624 | 112434 | 275 | 1500 | T3Cy. | 624 | |
| 1901 | Fernley | 3836 | WG | 647 | 113515 | 297 | 2000 | T3Cy. | 647 | |
| 1901 | Newlands | 3024 | WG | 652 | 115125 | 257 | 1500 | T3Cy. | 652 | |
| 1901 | Waverley | 2569 | WG | 639 | 114406 | 225 | 1250 | T3Cy. | 639 | |
| 1901 | Beechley | 3828 | WG | 645 | 113513 | 297 | 2000 | T3Cy. | 645 | |
| 1901 | Holmeside | 3833 | WG | 643 | 112450 | 322 | 2000 | T3Cy. | 643 | lost 26.8.1913 |
| 1902 | Svealand | 2934 | WG | 654 | Sweden | 297 | 1500 | T3Cy. | 654 | |
| 1902 | Drumbain / Houtdijk | 2313 | WG | 662 | 115833 | 226 | - | T3Cy. | 662 | |
| 1902 | Woodside | 445 | LO | 53 | 118019 | 183 | 1200 | 2T4Cy | 213 | Ferry: twin screw |
| 1902 | Ranza | 2320 | WG | 658 | 115797 | 222 | 1250 | T3Cy. | 658 | |
| 1902 | Ariel | 3427 | WG | 660 | 115132 | 284 | 1700 | T3Cy. | 660 | |
| 1902 | Rhodanthe | 3060 | WG | 657 | 115803 | 297 | 1500 | T3Cy. | 657 | |
| 1902 | Ville de Rouen | 4923 | FM | n.k. | France | 348 | 1600 | T3Cy. | 214 | Eng. assembly Caillard Freres |
| 1902 | Nolisement | 3228 | WG | 659 | 115375 | 297 | 2000 | T3Cy. | 659 | |
| 1902 | Normand | 2121 | WG | 663 | Norway | 218 | 1250 | T3Cy. | 663 | |
| 1902 | Bidston | 444 | LO | 52 | 118008 | 183 | 1200 | 2T4Cy | 212 | Ferry. Twin Screw. |
| 1902 | Spondilus | 7291 | WG | 656 | 118311 | 518 | 3000 | T3Cy. | 656 | Tanker |
| 1902 | Pectan | 7387 | WG | 655 | 115900 | 518 | 3000 | T3Cy. | 655 | Tanker |
| 1902 | Snel / Rossum | 1320 | BM | 145 | Holland | 148 | 800 | T3Cy. | 211 | |
| 1902 | Wermland / Bratland | 2308 | WG | 653 | Sweden | 194 | 1200 | T3Cy. | 653 | |
| 1902 | Antigua | 2875 | WG | 664 | 115146 | 297 | 1300 | T3Cy. | 664 | LR(04) 250NHP |
| 1902 | Hobart | 2542 | WG | 661 | 115138 | 231 | 1250 | T3Cy. | 661 | |
| 1903 | Camaguey/Tabaristan | 3462 | WG | 676 | 118713 | 376 | 2000 | T3Cy. | 676 | |
| 1903 | Queenborough | 2961 | WG | 672 | 118778 | 297 | 1500 | T3Cy. | 672 | |

| YEAR | SHIP | GRT | BLDR | YARD No. | OFF. No. | NHP | IHP | TYPE | ENG. No. | REMARKS |
|---|---|---|---|---|---|---|---|---|---|---|
| 1903 | Pandia A. Ralli | 2281 | WG | 665 | Greece | 222 | 1250 | T3Cy. | 665 | |
| 1903 | Bracondale | 2094 | WG | 674 | 115151 | 218 | 1200 | T3Cy. | 674 | 3150 DWT |
| 1903 | Cadiz 2 / Kiora | 2099 | CNE | 23 | Spain | 184 | - | T3Cy. | 210 ? | shipped per "Engineer" Aug.'02 |
| 1903 | Nunima | 2938 | WG | 671 | 115152 | 297 | 1700 | T3Cy. | 671 | |
| 1903 | Luristan / Antigua | 3432 | WG | 677 | 118714 | 376 | 2000 | T3Cy. | 677 | |
| 1903 | Margit Groedel | 2489 | WG | 670 | 118299 | 240 | 1300 | T3Cy. | 670 | LR(04) 252NHP |
| 1903 | Pedro Luis Lacave | 2129 | CNE | 24 | Spain | 184 | - | T3Cy. | 209 ? | shipped per "Engineer" Aug '02 |
| 1903 | Alicia | 2130 | WG | 675 | 115155 | 218 | 1200 | T3Cy. | 675 | |
| 1903 | Leonis / Bengalen | 2660 | WG | 673 | 115153 | 245 | 1300 | T3Cy. | 673 | |
| 1903 | Melanie Groedel | 3001 | WG | 668 | 118277 | 297 | 1600 | T3Cy. | 668 | |
| 1903 | Estonia / Kalo | 1967 | WG | 667 | Denmark | 180 | 1100 | T3Cy. | 667 | |
| 1903 | Mariner | 2378 | WG | 666 | 115148 | 240 | 1300 | T3Cy. | 666 | |
| 1903 | Longscar | 2583 | WG | 679 | 115159 | 240 | 1300 | T3Cy. | 679 | |
| 1903 | Longhirst | 3052 | WG | 678 | 118377 | 254 | 1500 | T3Cy. | 678 | |
| 1903 | Harald | 1970 | WG | 669 | Denmark | 194 | 1100 | T3Cy. | 669 | |
| 1904 | Arza-Mendi /Getso/Rola | 1235 | EU | 10 | Spain | 114 | - | T3Cy. | 217 | Blt 1866: Tripled CMEW 1904 |
| 1904 | Minia (Cable ship) | 2061 | LG | 116 | 56762 | 246 | 1000 | T3Cy. | 215 | For CMEW Power House. |
| 1904 | """Bradgate'""(Non-marine)" | — | — | — | ---- | | 650 | T3Cy. | 216 | LR(04) 270NHP |
| 1904 | Atlantic | 3016 | WG | 681 | 118804 | 294 | 1500 | T3Cy. | 681 | |
| 1904 | Ludwig Groedel | 2967 | WG | 685 | 118423 | 250 | 1300 | T3Cy. | 685 | |
| 1904 | Delta | 2363 | WG | 695 | Holland | 194 | 1200 | T3Cy. | 695 | |
| 1904 | Sverre | 3564 | WG | 680 | Norway | 290 | 1700 | T3Cy. | 680 | |
| 1904 | Kratos | 3532 | WG | 689 | Sweden | 335 | 2000 | T3Cy. | 689 | |
| 1904 | Uppland | 2399 | WG | 686 | Sweden | 250 | 1300 | T3Cy. | 686 | |
| 1904 | Southwaite | 3618 | WG | 683 | 115388 | 325 | 2000 | T3Cy. | 683 | |
| 1904 | Jethou | 4284 | WG | 697 | Norway | 372 | 2000 | T3Cy. | 697 | |
| 1904 | Leander | 2830 | WG | 694 | 120484 | 294 | - | T3Cy. | 694 | |
| 1904 | Runswick | 3060 | WG | 688 | 118471 | 254 | 1500 | T3Cy. | 688 | |
| 1904 | Ariadne | 3065 | WG | 690 | 118462 | 297 | 1500 | T3Cy. | 690 | |
| 1904 | Cober | 3060 | WG | 687 | 118455 | 254 | 1500 | T3Cy. | 687 | LR(04) 299 NHP |
| 1904 | Gisella Groedel | 2502 | WG | 684 | 118402 | 240 | 1300 | T3Cy. | 684 | LR(04) 255NHP |
| 1904 | Eastwood | 3502 | WG | 692 | 115170 | 296 | 1700 | T3Cy. | 692 | |
| 1904 | Arza Mendi | | ? | n.k. | Spain | | 500 | T3Cy. | 217 | Shipped per "Baiko" 1905 |
| 1904 | Rags | 3641 | WG | 693 | Norway | 291 | 1700 | T3Cy. | 693 | |
| 1904 | """Tunstall""(Non-marine)" | — | — | — | ---- | | 650 | T3Cy. | 218 | For CMEW Power House. |

| YEAR | SHIP | GRT | BLDR | YARD No. | OFF. No. | NHP | IHP | TYPE | ENG. No. | REMARKS |
|------|------|-----|------|----------|----------|-----|-----|------|----------|---------|
| 1904 | Teutonic | 3603 | WG | 696 | 118849 | 303 | 2000 | T3Cy. | 696 | |
| 1904 | Britannic | 3486 | WG | 682 | 118811 | 284 | 1700 | T3Cy. | 682 | |
| 1904 | Iolanthe | 3081 | WG | 691 | 118485 | 294 | 1500 | T3Cy. | 691 | |
| 1905 | Havre | 2073 | WG | 713 | 118720 | 274 | 1250 | T3Cy. | 713 | |
| 1905 | Turkistan / Ekbatana | 4505 | WG | 698 | 118717 | 506 | 3000 | T3Cy. | 698 | |
| 1905 | Chelford | 2995 | WG | 716 | 119891 | 280 | 1500 | T3Cy. | 716 | Sunk 14.4.1918 |
| 1905 | Twilight | 3100 | WG | 708 | 119885 | 283 | 1500 | T3Cy. | 708 | |
| 1905 | not known | | SHT | 324 | — | | 650 | T3Cy. | 219 | |
| 1905 | Northwaite | 3626 | WG | 712 | 119979 | 300 | 2000 | T3Cy. | 712 | |
| 1905 | Cambyses | 3190 | WG | 705 | 119873 | 291 | 1700 | T3Cy. | 705 | |
| 1905 | Domira | 3130 | WG | 707 | 121255 | 283 | 1500 | T3Cy. | 707 | |
| 1905 | Westlands | 3112 | WG | 703 | 119872 | 283 | 1500 | T3Cy. | 703 | Sunk 23.11.1917 |
| 1905 | Eastlands | 3113 | WG | 702 | 119868 | 283 | 1500 | T3Cy. | 702 | Sunk 25.1.1918 |
| 1905 | Gorjistan / Persepolis | 4519 | WG | 699 | 118718 | 506 | 3000 | T3Cy. | 699 | |
| 1905 | Manchuria | 2996 | WG | 704 | 119877 | 254 | 1500 | T3Cy. | 704 | LR(1911) 280NHP. Sunk 17.10.17 |
| 1905 | Wavelet | 2992 | WG | 701 | 119866 | 280 | 1500 | T3Cy. | 701 | |
| 1905 | Cynthiana | 3185 | WG | 706 | 119884 | 291 | 1700 | T3Cy. | 706 | |
| 1905 | Harlech | 3494 | WG | 710 | 120614 | 316 | 2000 | T3Cy. | 710 | |
| 1905 | Pruth | 4407 | WG | 700 | 120529 | 348 | 2000 | T3Cy. | 700 | Sunk 9.10.1914 |
| 1905 | Drumloist | 3118 | WG | 711 | 120602 | 307 | 1700 | T3Cy. | 711 | Sunk 24.6.1915 |
| 1905 | Harlingen | 3470 | WG | 709 | 120606 | 316 | 2000 | T3Cy. | 709 | |
| 1906 | Dan | 1871 | WG | 726 | Denmark | 199 | - | T3Cy. | 726 | |
| 1906 | Trinity | 3803 | WG | 722 | 123019 | 334 | - | T3Cy. | 722 | |
| 1906 | Aagot | 3960 | WG | 725 | Norway | 289 | - | T3Cy. | 725 | |
| 1906 | Skogland | 2927 | WG | 734 | Sweden | 280 | - | T3Cy. | 734 | |
| 1906 | Monaro | 2656 | WG | 718 | 119892 | 231 | - | T3Cy. | 718 | |
| 1906 | Harperley | 3990 | WG | 717 | 120666 | 358 | - | T3Cy. | 717 | |
| 1906 | Saint Paul ? | | CHF | n.k. | France ? | 199 | | T3Cy. | 224 | CASTINGS SENT. |
| 1906 | Buxton | 3142 | WG | 724 | 123249 | 270 | - | T3Cy. | 724 | |
| 1906 | Antiope | 2972 | WG | 727 | 123678 | 279 | - | T3Cy. | 727 | Sunk 9.8.1916 |
| 1906 | Marchioness of Bute | 4294 | WG | 720 | 123157 | 363 | - | T3Cy. | 720 | |
| 1906 | Veraston | 1979 | WG | 739 | 124318 | 167 | - | T3Cy. | 739 | |
| 1906 | St Pierre ? | | CHF | n.k. | France ? | | | T3Cy. | 225 | CASTINGS SENT. |
| 1906 | Harewood | 3106 | WG | 723 | 120686 | 277 | | T3Cy. | 723 | |
| 1906 | Rubens | 3587 | WG | 719 | 120678 | 280 | - | T3Cy. | 719 | |

| YEAR | SHIP | GRT | BLDR | YARD No. | OFF. No. | NHP | IHP | TYPE | ENG. No. | REMARKS |
|------|------|-----|------|----------|----------|-----|-----|------|----------|---------|
| 1906 | Stegelborg | 1885 | WG | 729 | Denmark | 185 | - | T3Cy. | 729 | |
| 1906 | Harlyn | 3459 | WG | 731 | 123704 | 316 | - | T3Cy. | 731 | |
| 1906 | Llanwern | 4290 | WG | 721 | 123160 | 363 | - | T3Cy. | 721 | |
| 1906 | Saint Rene / Headley | 4238 | WG | 737 | 123779 | 408 | - | T3Cy. | 737 | |
| 1906 | Alexandra | 2977 | WG | 733 | 109730 | 380 | - | T3Cy. | 733 | |
| 1906 | Saint Luc | 2456 | CHF | n.k. | France | 156 | - | T3Cy. | 222 | CASTINGS TO DUNKIRK.B'lt 1908 |
| 1906 | Tangistan | 3737 | WG | 736 | 124358 | 301 | - | T3Cy. | 736 | Sunk 9.3.1915 |
| 1906 | Cresswell | 3257 | WG | 730 | 123679 | 287 | - | T3Cy. | 730 | |
| 1906 | Ulfe | 1869 | WG | 728 | Denmark | 200 | - | T3Cy. | 728 | |
| 1906 | Mathilda | 4051 | WG | 732 | Norway | 348 | - | T3Cy. | 732 | |
| 1906 | Dirphys | 2795 | WG | 740 | Germany | 294 | - | T3Cy. | 740 | |
| 1906 | Saint Jean (Trawler) | 287 | CHF | 34 | France | 60 | | T3Cy. | 221 | CASTINGS SENT TO DUNKIRK. |
| 1906 | Ben Lomond | 2813 | WG | 735 | 122863 | 287 | - | T3Cy. | 735 | Sunk 7.7.1918 |
| 1906 | Ravelston | 2085 | WG | 738 | 90925 | 219 | - | T3Cy. | 738 | Scrapped in 1959, aged 53. |
| 1907 | Hartington | 4043 | WG | 747 | 125598 | 358 | 2000 | T3Cy. | 747 | |
| 1907 | Maylands | 3854 | WG | 750 | 124343 | 316 | 2000 | T3Cy. | 750 | |
| 1907 | Frizos | 3521 | WG | 746 | 125585 | 350 | 2000 | T3Cy. | 746 | LR(06) 323NHP |
| 1907 | Magyarorszag | 3661 | WG | 742 | Aust-Hung | 292 | 1700 | T3Cy. | 742 | |
| 1907 | Ivar | 2134 | WG | 749 | Denmark | 235 | 1250 | T3Cy. | 749 | |
| 1907 | Pollacsek | 3691 | WG | 744 | Aust-Hung | 292 | 1700 | T3Cy. | 744 | |
| 1907 | Szterenyi | 3669 | WG | 741 | Aust-Hung | 292 | 1700 | T3Cy. | 741 | |
| 1907 | Saint Andre (Trawler) | 286 | CHF | 53 | France | 60 | - | T3Cy. | 220 | CASTINGS SENT TO DUNKIRK. |
| 1907 | Despina G. Michalinos | 2827 | WG | 745 | Greece | 280 | 1500 | T3Cy. | 745 | LR(06) 292NHP |
| 1907 | Grof Serenyi Bela | 3628 | WG | 743 | Aust-Hung | 292 | 1700 | T3Cy. | 743 | LR (06) 391NHP |
| 1907 | Welbury | 3590 | WG | 748 | 124341 | 280 | 1700 | T3Cy. | 748 | |
| 1907 | Romsdal | 3157 | WG | 751 | Norway | 280 | 1400 | T3Cy. | 751 | |
| 1907 | Whitby Abbey | 1188 | WG | 755 | 128091 | 504 | 3400 | T3Cy. | 755 | |
| 1907 | Sainte Adresse ? | | CHN | 113 | France | 265 | | T3Cy. | 229 | CASTINGS SENT. |
| 1907 | Selja | 4448 | WG | 752 | Norway | 360 | 2000 | T3Cy. | 752 | |
| 1908 | not known | | ? | n.k. | France ? | | 700 | T3Cy. | 231 | CASTINGS SENT |
| 1908 | Fameliaris | 3189 | WG | 754 | Greece | 277 | - | T3Cy. | 754 | |
| 1908 | Stigstad | 4633 | WG | 757 | Norway | 350 | - | T3Cy. | 757 | |
| 1908 | Saranac | 5316 | WG | 753 | 127433 | 427 | - | T3Cy. | 753 | Tanker |
| 1908 | Kapunda | 3096 | WG | 758 | 127437 | 497 | - | T3Cy. | 758 | |
| 1908 | not known | | ? | n.k. | France ? | | 700 | T3Cy. | 232 | CASTINGS SENT |

| YEAR | SHIP | GRT | BLDR | YARD No. | OFF. No. | NHP | IHP | TYPE | ENG. No. | REMARKS |
|------|------|-----|------|----------|----------|-----|-----|------|----------|---------|
| 1908 | Jervaulx Abbey | 1188 | WG | 756 | 128094 | 504 | - | T3Cy. | 756 | |
| 1908 | Saint Marc | 2456 | CHF | 49 | France | 156 | - | T3Cy. | 223 | CASTINGS SENT. |
| 1908 | Norburn | 2023 | CT | 131 | 127435 | 210 | - | T3Cy. | 228 | Ex No.105: salvaged 1899 & rebuilt. |
| 1909 | Eretza Mendi | 4126 | WG | 761 | Spain | 379 | - | T3Cy. | 761 | |
| 1909 | Caterino | 3728 | WG | 765 | 127445 | 274 | - | T3Cy. | 765 | |
| 1909 | Rossano | 3744 | WG | 763 | 127442 | 274 | - | T3Cy. | 763 | |
| 1909 | Harpeake | 4600 | WG | 764 | 129034 | 370 | - | T3Cy. | 764 | |
| 1909 | Bjornsterne Bjornson | 5268 | WG | 762 | Norway | 339 | - | T3Cy. | 762 | |
| 1909 | Breynton | 4267 | WG | 766 | 128497 | 370 | - | T3Cy. | 766 | |
| 1909 | Harfleur / Georgina | 4523 | WG | 759 | 125753 | 391 | - | T3Cy. | 759 | |
| 1909 | Hargrove | 1631 | WG | 767 | 129060 | 220 | - | T3Cy. | 767 | |
| 1909 | Paul Leferne | 306 | CHA | 53 | France | 36 | - | T3Cy. | 230 | "Baliseur type" |
| 1909 | Ocean Queen | 3194 | WG | 760 | Norway | 348 | - | T3Cy. | 760 | |
| 1909 | Rachel / Grelarlie | 3580 | WG | 768 | 129066 | 344 | 1900 | T3Cy. | 768 | |
| 1910 | Zinovia | 2556 | WG | 769 | Greece | 292 | 1550 | T3Cy. | 769 | |
| 1910 | Djerissa | 3623 | WG | 773 | 128910 | 320 | 1750 | T3Cy. | 773 | |
| 1910 | Baltistan / Saros | 3304 | WG | 777 | 128911 | 386 | 2150 | T3Cy. | 777 | |
| 1910 | Harpagus | 5865 | WG | 771 | 129100 | 574 | 3500 | T3Cy. | 771 | Sunk 9.5.1917 |
| 1910 | Fridland | 4926 | WG | 775 | Sweden | 450 | 2250 | T3Cy. | 775 | |
| 1910 | Ryburn | 2985 | WG | 780 | 127462 | 287 | 1830 | T3Cy. | 780 | |
| 1910 | Crawley Incline | | NER | | | | 250 | T3Cy. | 233 | Hauling engine: Non-Marine |
| 1910 | Mohacsfield | 3677 | WG | 770 | 127454 | 335 | 1650 | T3Cy. | 770 | Sunk 7.1.1917 |
| 1910 | Escrick | 4151 | WG | 781 | 129157 | 342 | 1750 | T3Cy. | 781 | Sunk 16.8.1918 |
| 1910 | Camerata | 3729 | WG | 774 | 128912 | 320 | 1750 | T3Cy. | 774 | |
| 1910 | Boukadra | 3722 | WG | 776 | 128915 | 320 | 1750 | T3Cy. | 776 | |
| 1910 | Harpalion | 5686 | WG | 779 | 129152 | 574 | 3500 | T3Cy. | 779 | Sunk 24.2.1915 |
| 1910 | Joseph Chamberlain | 3709 | WG | 772 | 127461 | 280 | 1800 | T3Cy. | 772 | LR(11) 336NHP |
| 1910 | Registan | 3349 | WG | 778 | 128914 | 386 | 2150 | T3Cy. | 778 | |
| 1911 | Turkistan | 4552 | WG | 797 | 128929 | 606 | 3830 | T3Cy. | 797 | |
| 1911 | August | 5254 | WG | 783 | Norway | 339 | 2740 | T3Cy. | 783 | |
| 1911 | Roselands | 4408 | WG | 793 | 132802 | 408 | 2420 | T3Cy. | 793 | |
| 1911 | Ruysdael | 3477 | WG | 800 | 132653 | 298 | 1560 | T3Cy. | 800 | sunk 7.9.1918 |
| 1911 | Arna | 5264 | WG | 784 | Norway | 368 | 2740 | T3Cy. | 784 | |
| 1911 | Tilemachos | 3562 | WG | 787 | Greece | 324 | 1680 | T3Cy. | 787 | |
| 1911 | Armanistan | 3871 | WG | 786 | 128920 | 386 | 2330 | T3Cy. | 786 | |

| YEAR | SHIP | GRT | BLDR | YARD No. | OFF. No. | NHP | IHP | TYPE | ENG. No. | REMARKS |
|------|------|-----|------|----------|----------|-----|-----|------|----------|---------|
| 1911 | Craigston | 2616 | WG | 790 | 128529 | 251 | 1340 | T3Cy. | 790 | Sunk 4.10.1915 |
| 1911 | Harpalyce | 5940 | WG | 789 | 132551 | 339 | 2700 | T3Cy. | 789 | Sunk 10.4.1915 |
| 1911 | Langholm / Madras City | 4167 | WG | 782 | 129196 | 342 | 1750 | T3Cy. | 782 | |
| 1911 | Gorjistan | 4603 | WG | 794 | 128925 | 616 | 3820 | T3Cy. | 794 | |
| 1911 | Daybreak | 3238 | WG | 796 | 132809 | 330 | 1740 | T3Cy. | 796 | sunk 24.12.1917 |
| 1911 | Normanby | 4219 | WG | 792 | 132596 | 412 | 2360 | T3Cy. | 792 | |
| 1911 | Robert Coverdale | 3722 | WG | 798 | 132803 | 336 | 1800 | T3Cy. | 798 | |
| 1911 | Hans B. | 4253 | WG | 785 | Norway | 381 | 2040 | T3Cy. | 785 | |
| 1911 | Otto Trechmann | 3736 | WG | 791 | 132806 | 358 | 2020 | T3Cy. | 791 | |
| 1911 | Penhale | 3711 | WG | 795 | 128438 | 336 | 1800 | T3Cy. | 795 | sunk 18.5.1917 |
| 1911 | Brooklet | 3112 | WG | 788 | 132801 | 309 | 1670 | T3Cy. | 788 | |
| 1912 | Thorpwood | 3183 | WG | 799 | 128815 | 278 | 1400 | T3Cy. | 799 | sunk 8.10.1915 |
| 1912 | CMEW Power House | — | — | — | — | 550 | T3Cy. | 245 | Non-Marine for works use. |
| 1912 | Arakan / Cap Comorin | 5146 | WG | 811 | Holland | 623 | 3910 | T3Cy. | 811 | |
| 1912 | Oakfield | 3646 | WG | 801 | 132816 | 317 | 2030 | T3Cy. | 801 | |
| 1912 | Shahristan /Zuiderdijk | 5211 | WG | 805 | 128934 | 603 | 3710 | T3Cy. | 805 | |
| 1912 | Arachne | 3917 | WG | 813 | 132832 | 337 | 1800 | T3Cy. | 813 | |
| 1912 | Flixton | 4303 | WG | 807 | 133404 | 404 | 2280 | T3Cy. | 807 | |
| 1912 | Marguerite | 3236 | WG | 804 | France | 309 | 1670 | T3Cy. | 804 | |
| 1912 | Mokta | 3934 | WG | 815 | 128937 | 320 | 1750 | T3Cy. | 815 | |
| 1912 | Confield | 2804 | WG | 809 | 133515 | 267 | 1390 | T3Cy. | 809 | |
| 1912 | Arabistan / Chinwarh | 5192 | WG | 802 | 128930 | 603 | 3710 | T3Cy. | 802 | |
| 1912 | Batjan | 6354 | WG | 819 | Holland | 621 | 4000 | T3Cy. | 819 | |
| 1912 | Quebra | 4528 | WG | 803 | 132673 | 493 | 2180 | T3Cy. | 803 | |
| 1912 | Cyrena | 2138 | WG | 818 | 135184 | 270 | 1460 | T3Cy. | 818 | Tanker ? |
| 1912 | Boscastle | 2346 | WG | 812 | 132828 | 261 | 1440 | T3Cy. | 812 | sunk 7.9.1918 |
| 1912 | Weatherhill Incline | — | NER | — | — | | | T3Cy. | 247 | Hauling engine: Non-marine. |
| 1912 | Tabarka | 3933 | WG | 817 | 128938 | 320 | 1750 | T3Cy. | 817 | |
| 1912 | Baharistan | 3629 | WG | 814 | 128935 | 359 | 2030 | T3Cy. | 814 | |
| 1912 | Burma | 5408 | WG | 808 | Aust-Hung | 493 | 3030 | T3Cy. | 808 | |
| 1912 | Harden | 1683 | WG | 810 | 132719 | 202 | 1170 | T3Cy. | 810 | |
| 1912 | Boeton | 6403 | WG | 816 | Holland | 621 | 4000 | T3Cy. | 816 | |
| 1912 | Penolver | 3721 | WG | 806 | 133334 | 336 | 1800 | T3Cy. | 806 | |
| 1913 | Saint Vincent ? | | ? | n.k. | France | | 1550 | T3Cy. | 237 | CASTINGS SENT. |
| 1913 | Saint Simon ? | | AC | n.k. | France | | 1550 | T3Cy. | 236 | CASTINGS SENT. |

| YEAR | SHIP | GRT | BLDR | YARD No. | OFF. No. | NHP | IHP | TYPE | ENG. No. | REMARKS |
|---|---|---|---|---|---|---|---|---|---|---|
| 1913 | Ubier | 2889 | WG | 838 | Belgium | 288 | 1590 | T3Cy. | 838 | |
| 1913 | Orna | 4783 | WG | 830 | 136261 | 588 | 3980 | T3Cy. | 830 | |
| 1913 | Oceanos | 4814 | WG | 832 | Greece | 422 | 2450 | T3Cy. | 832 | 12 knots. |
| 1913 | Saint Michel ? | | AC | n.k. | France | | 2740 | T3Cy. | 239 | ENGINE SENT OUT. |
| 1913 | not known | | AC | n.k. | France | | 1050 | T3Cy. | 234 | CASTINGS SENT. |
| 1913 | Muristan | 2886 | WG | 831 | 128946 | 288 | 1248 | T3Cy. | 831 | |
| 1913 | Noorderdyk | 7156 | WG | 820 | Holland | 625 | 3980 | T3Cy. | 820 | |
| 1913 | Nigaristan / Portloe | 4345 | WG | 835 | 128949 | 371 | 2040 | T3Cy. | 835 | |
| 1913 | Saint Louis ? | | AC | n.k. | France | | 2740 | T3Cy. | 238 | CASTINGS SENT. |
| 1913 | Penhallow | 4318 | WG | 828 | 133343 | 371 | 2040 | T3Cy. | 828 | sunk 12.6.1918 |
| 1913 | Hackness | 4927 | WG | 834 | 135311 | 371 | 2820 | T3Cy. | 834 | |
| 1913 | Arabistan / Chinkoa | 5222 | WG | 827 | 128943 | 588 | 3980 | T3Cy. | 827 | |
| 1913 | Pensilva | 4313 | WG | 824 | 133342 | 371 | 2040 | T3Cy. | 824 | |
| 1913 | Saint Chamond | 3077 | WG | 821 | France | 267 | 1430 | T3Cy. | 821 | sunk 30.4.1918 |
| 1913 | Penmorvah | 4336 | WG | 833 | 133347 | 378 | 2040 | T3Cy. | 833 | |
| 1913 | Ozarda | 4791 | WG | 822 | 133114 | 603 | 4125 | T3Cy. | 822 | |
| 1913 | Dunsley | 4930 | WG | 829 | 135272 | 422 | 2820 | T3Cy. | 829 | sunk 19.8.1915 |
| 1913 | Nominoe | 3203 | WG | 826 | France | 289 | 1590 | T3Cy. | 826 | |
| 1913 | Banka | 6665 | WG | 836 | Holland | 656 | 4570 | T3Cy. | 836 | |
| 1913 | Saint Philippe ? | | AC | n.k. | France | | 1550 | T3Cy. | 235 | CASTINGS SENT. |
| 1913 | Kathlamba | 6382 | WG | 825 | 133316 | 586 | 3820 | T3Cy. | 825 | |
| 1913 | City of Norwich | 6726 | WG | 823 | 135479 | 606 | 4030 | T3Cy. | 823 | |
| 1914 | Ricardo A. Mestres | 4468 | WG | 839 | 136686 | 320 | 2370 | T3Cy. | 839 | Tanker: 6240DWT 10+ Knots. |
| 1914 | Firfield | 4028 | WG | 851 | 135916 | 401 | 1840 | T3Cy. | 851 | sunk 16.7.1917 |
| 1914 | Ribera | 3510 | WG | 853 | 136776 | 299 | - | T3Cy. | 853 | sunk 10.6.1917 |
| 1914 | Nolisement | 4447 | WG | 841 | 136737 | 430 | 2630 | T3Cy. | 841 | |
| 1914 | Drubja | 3841 | WG | 843 | Russia | 371 | 2050 | T3Cy. | 843 | |
| 1914 | City of Rangoon | 6635 | WG | 842 | 135582 | 617 | 4150 | T3Cy. | 842 | |
| 1914 | Rosenborg | 1997 | WG | 844 | Denmark | 188 | 1010 | T3Cy. | 844 | |
| 1914 | Rosalie | 4236 | WG | 860 | 136982 | 388 | 2210 | T3Cy. | 860 | sunk 20.2.1917 |
| 1914 | City of Newcastle | 7032 | WG | 852 | 137421 | 616 | - | T3Cy. | 852 | |
| 1914 | Arnold Maersk | 1366 | WG | 840 | Denmark | 188 | 1010 | T3Cy. | 840 | 3250 DWT |
| 1914 | Orama | 4742 | WG | 845 | 136305 | 588 | 3980 | T3Cy. | 845 | |
| 1914 | Unbe Mendi | 4313 | EU | 32 | Spain | 382 | 1550 | T3Cy. | 240 | |
| 1914 | Boeroe | 6591 | WG | 837 | Holland | 656 | 4570 | T3Cy. | 837 | |

| YEAR | SHIP | GRT | BLDR | YARD No. | OFF. No. | NHP | IHP | TYPE | ENG. No. | REMARKS |
|---|---|---|---|---|---|---|---|---|---|---|
| 1914 | Prikonisos | 3537 | WG | 849 | Greece | 336 | 1800 | T3Cy. | 849 | |
| 1914 | Nirvana | 6044 | WG | 847 | 136329 | 656 | 4570 | T3Cy. | 847 | |
| 1914 | Rosalie | 4242 | WG | 850 | 136965 | 388 | 1734 | T3Cy. | 850 | sunk 10.8.1915 |
| 1914 | Chilkana | 5146 | WG | 846 | 136315 | 589 | 3980 | T3Cy. | 846 | |
| 1914 | Skjoldborg | 1954 | WG | 848 | Denmark | 198 | 1010 | T3Cy. | 848 | |
| 1914 | M.15 HMS | 540 D | WG | 865 | Admiralty | - | 800 | T6Cy. | 865 | Monitor.Twin Screw. Torp.1917. |
| 1915 | Eastgate | 4277 | WG | 861 | 139100 | 421 | - | T3Cy. | 861 | |
| 1915 | City of Oran | 7395 | WG | 856 | 137804 | 628 | - | T3Cy. | 856 | |
| 1915 | Mar Mediterraneo | 2896 | EU | 33 | Spain | 268 | - | T3Cy. | 241 | |
| 1915 | M.17 / Toedjoe(tanker) | 540 D | WG | 871 | Admiralty | - | 800 | T6Cy. | 871 | Monitor.Twin Screw. |
| 1915 | Mar del Norte | 2917 | EU | 34 | Spain | 268 | - | T3Cy. | 242 | |
| 1915 | M.16 / Tiga (tanker) | 540 D | WG | 866 | Admiralty | - | 800 | T6Cy. | 866 | Monitor.Twin Screw. |
| 1915 | Hawsker / Sheaf Mead | 4273 | WG | 858 | 137072 | 421 | - | T3Cy. | 858 | |
| 1915 | Wordsworth | 3509 | WG | 854 | 136807 | 299 | - | T3Cy. | 854 | sunk 11.3.1917 |
| 1915 | M.18 / Anam (tanker) | 540 D | WG | 872 | Admiralty | - | 800 | Motor | — | Monitor. Twin Screw. |
| 1915 | Harlow / Narocz | 1975 | WG | 859 | 139062 | 202 | - | T3Cy. | 859 | |
| 1915 | City of Hankow | 7369 | WG | 857 | 137452 | 738 | - | Quad. | 857 | |
| 1915 | Harlyn | 1794 | WG | 855 | 136848 | 202 | - | T3Cy. | 855 | sunk 9.2.1916 |
| 1916 | City of Manila | 7479 | WG | 863 | 137508 | 745 | - | Quad. | 863 | |
| 1916 | P.29 | 692 D | WG | 876 | Admiralty | - | 3500 | Turb. | 876 | Shaft HP shown. Patrol vsl. |
| 1916 | Wilton | 4283 | WG | 867 | 139221 | 241 | - | T3Cy. | 867 | sunk 10.1.1918 |
| 1916 | Nirpura | 7640 | WG | 862 | 137818 | 558 | - | T3Cy. | 862 | sunk 16.4.1918 |
| 1916 | Arlington / Carmarthen | 4262 | WG | 868 | 139598 | 404 | - | T3Cy. | 868 | 1st lift at 100T crane 12/9/16 |
| 1916 | Andree | 3689 | WG | 864 | 136983 | 378 | - | T3Cy. | 864 | |
| 1916 | Mouro | 2905 | EU | 36 | Spain | 268 | - | T3Cy. | 243 | |
| 1917 | City of Lucknow | 8292 | WG | 873 | 140515 | 758 | 2450 | Quad. | 873 | sunk 21.12.1917 |
| 1917 | P.45 | 692 D | WG | 885 | Admiralty | - | 3500 | Turb. | 885 | IHP=Shaft HP. Patrol vsl. |
| 1917 | Rapidol | 2648 | WG | 886 | 140332 | 545 | - | T3Cy. | 886 | Tanker. |
| 1917 | Cresswell / Guldborg | 2829 | WG | 874 | 137048 | 288 | 1248 | T3Cy. | 874 | sunk 5.2.1918 |
| 1917 | P.30 | 692 D | WG | 877 | Admiralty | - | 3500 | Turb. | 877 | Shaft HP shown. Patrol vsl. |
| 1917 | Gypol / Pearleaf | 5911 | WG | 878 | 140269 | 1089 | - | T6Cy | 878 | RFA Tanker. Twin screw. |
| 1917 | City of Adelaide | 8388 | WG | 869 | 137546 | 745 | - | Quad. | 869 | Sunk 11.8.1918 |
| 1917 | Luis | 4284 | WG | 870 | 139829 | 421 | - | T3Cy. | 870 | sunk 12.4.1918 |
| 1917 | Mar Tirreno | 3367 | EU | 37 | Spain | 268 | - | T3Cy. | 244 | |
| 1917 | Merioneth | 3003 | WG | 875 | 148272 | 436 | - | T3Cy. | 875 | |

| YEAR | SHIP | GRT | BLDR | YARD No. | OFF. No. | NHP | IHP | TYPE | ENG. No. | REMARKS |
|---|---|---|---|---|---|---|---|---|---|---|
| 1917 | Anglesea | 4460 | WG | 888 | 139625 | 434 | - | T3Cy. | 888 | Sunk 24.4.1917 |
| 1917 | Montenol | 2646 | WG | 887 | 140408 | 545 | - | T3Cy. | 887 | R.F.A. Tanker. |
| 1918 | War Subadar | 5563 | WG | 903 | 142629 | 517 | - | T3Cy. | 903 | |
| 1918 | War Shell / Brenta | 2366 | WG | 901 | 142585 | 266 | - | T3Cy. | 901 | |
| 1918 | War Crag / Wye Crag | 3110 | WG | 905 | 142626 | 430 | - | T3Cy. | 905 | |
| 1918 | War Torpedo / Parame | 2285 | WG | 900 | 142458 | 266 | - | T3Cy. | 900 | |
| 1918 | War Linnet/Moncalieri | 5267 | CT | 212 | 142725 | 212 | 1700 | T3Cy. | 254 | |
| 1918 | City of Florence | 6862 | WG | 879 | 140559 | 621 | - | T3Cy. | 879 | |
| 1918 | War Oasis / Oakwin | 3099 | WG | 914 | 142770 | 385 | - | T3Cy. | 914 | |
| 1918 | War Arabis | 5187 | WG | 896 | 142296 | 517 | - | T3Cy. | 896 | sunk 9.9.1918 |
| 1918 | City of Birmingham | 6182 | WG | 881 | 137857 | 518 | - | T3Cy. | 881 | |
| 1918 | War Country / Ballara | 3335 | WG | 894 | 142350 | 426 | - | T3Cy. | 894 | |
| 1918 | War File /Sierra Madre | 2362 | AUS | 296 | 142591 | 410 | - | T3Cy. | 250 | |
| 1918 | War Wagtail /Vindelia | 4430 | WG | 906 | 142653 | 517 | - | T3Cy. | 906 | |
| 1918 | Respond | 800 | AYR | 480 | 148047 | 372 | - | T6Cy | 248 | Tug - twin screw |
| 1918 | War Mango / Warcuta | 2499 | WG | 908 | 142658 | 266 | - | T3Cy. | 908 | |
| 1918 | War Valley | 3104 | WG | 904 | 142603 | 385 | - | T3Cy. | 904 | Wrecked 16.2.1919 |
| 1918 | Kurdistan | 4289 | WG | 892 | 140708 | 437 | - | T3Cy. | 892 | |
| 1918 | Kioto | 4397 | WG | 880 | 140571 | 384 | - | T3Cy. | 880 | |
| 1918 | City of Corinth | 6173 | WG | 884 | 140555 | 581 | - | T3Cy. | 884 | |
| 1918 | War Pike | 5220 | WG | 898 | 142389 | 517 | - | T3Cy. | 898 | |
| 1918 | War Sepoy | 5557 | WG | 909 | 142773 | 517 | - | T3Cy. | 909 | |
| 1918 | War Jackdaw/Tartar Pr. | 5214 | WG | 899 | 142439 | 517 | - | T3Cy. | 899 | |
| 1918 | Capitan Segarra | 2252 | EU | 38 | Spain | 248 | - | T3Cy. | 246 | |
| 1918 | War Sikh/British Soldr | 5564 | WG | 907 | 142707 | 517 | - | T3Cy. | 907 | Tanker. |
| 1918 | War Foam / Kaikori | 3096 | WG | 895 | 142416 | 385 | - | T3Cy. | 895 | |
| 1918 | War Apricot /Sebastian | 2501 | WG | 912 | 142677 | 266 | - | T3Cy. | 912 | |
| 1918 | P.37 | 692 D | EU | 882 | Admiralty | - | 3500 | Turb. | 882 | IHP=Shaft HP. Patrol vsl. |
| 1918 | Resolve | 801 | AYR | 479 | 142766 | 372 | - | T6Cy. | 249 | Tug - twin screw |
| 1918 | War Crocus | 5296 | WG | 902 | 142467 | 417 | - | T3Cy. | 902 | sunk 8.7.1918 |
| 1918 | War Torrent/Cosmos Don | 3107 | WG | 910 | 142727 | 430 | - | T3Cy. | 910 | |
| 1919 | War Griffin / Gondia | 6553 | WG | 918 | 141936 | 517 | 3100 | T3Cy. | 918 | |
| 1919 | War Currant /Leicester | 2505 | WG | 916 | 143063 | 266 | 1590 | T3Cy. | 916 | |
| 1919 | Arno-Mendi | 5754 | EU | 49 | Spain | 461 | 1700 | T3Cy. | 258 | |
| 1919 | Saint Firmin | 4356 | WG | 927 | France | 515 | 3090 | T3Cy. | 927 | oilfired |

| YEAR | SHIP | GRT | BLDR | YARD No. | OFF. No. | NHP | IHP | TYPE | ENG. No. | REMARKS |
|------|------|-----|------|----------|----------|-----|-----|------|----------|---------|
| 1919 | War Bat / Garada | 5333 | EG | 932 | 141933 | 517 | 3100 | T3Cy. | 932 | |
| 1919 | War Globe/Adm.Hastings | 3054 | WG | 921 | 143320 | 357 | 2150 | T3Cy. | 921 | |
| 1919 | Sarthe | 5271 | WG | 923 | 144389 | 517 | 3100 | T3Cy. | 923 | |
| 1919 | War Bulldog / Tregenna | 5243 | WG | 915 | 142570 | 517 | 3100 | T3Cy. | 915 | |
| 1919 | Cretebow | 306 | AFC | n.k. | 143408 | 83 | - | T3Cy. | 252 | Tug. |
| 1919 | Cretehawser | 267 | WC | 1 | 143118 | 120 | - | T3Cy. | 251 | |
| 1919 | Western Valleys | 3106 | ARM | 953 | 136157 | 430 | 2580 | T3Cy. | 255 | |
| 1919 | Saint Ambroise | 3079 | WG | 929 | France | 414 | 2490 | T3Cy. | 929 | oilfired |
| 1919 | War Redtail / Homayun | 4514 | WG | 913 | 143404 | 517 | 3100 | T3Cy. | 913 | |
| 1919 | Fabian | 3059 | WG | 925 | 140655 | 407 | 2450 | T3Cy. | 925 | |
| 1919 | War Owl / Golconda | 5318 | EG | 931 | 141919 | 517 | 3100 | T3Cy. | 931 | |
| 1919 | Kara | 2478 | WG | 926 | 136156 | 266 | 1590 | T3Cy. | 926 | |
| 1919 | War Fly / Garbeta | 5333 | EG | 933 | 144195 | 517 | 3100 | T3Cy. | 933 | |
| 1919 | Grodno | 2452 | WG | 922 | 139340 | 266 | 1590 | T3Cy. | 922 | Scrapped 1968. |
| 1919 | War Midge / Romeo | 5157 | WG | 911 | 140630 | 517 | 3100 | T3Cy. | 911 | |
| 1919 | War Lurcher/Bondowoso | 5106 | WG | 917 | Holland | 517 | 3100 | T3Cy. | 917 | |
| 1919 | Creterope | 267 | WC | n.k. | 143300 | 120 | 720 | T3Cy. | 253 | Tug. |
| 1920 | Nirpura | 5961 | WG | 893 | 146257 | 656 | - | T3Cy. | 893 | |
| 1920 | Horda | 4301 | WG | 928 | Norway | 413 | - | T3Cy. | 928 | |
| 1920 | Saint Camille | 3274 | WG | 935 | France | 414 | - | T3Cy. | 935 | oilfired |
| 1920 | Saint Prosper | 3079 | WG | 930 | France | 515 | - | T3Cy. | 930 | oilfired |
| 1920 | Saint Rene / Avristan | 4453 | WG | 937 | 146669 | 515 | - | T3Cy. | 937 | |
| 1920 | Saint Roger / Registan | 4449 | WG | 938 | 146678 | 515 | - | T3Cy. | 938 | LR(26) 2 boilers ? |
| 1920 | Baarn / Cairnavon | 5245 | WG | 924 | Holland | 513 | - | T3Cy. | 924 | |
| 1920 | War Moth / Jeypore | 5318 | EG | 934 | 137273 | 517 | - | T3Cy. | 934 | |
| 1920 | Karonga /City of Derby | 6616 | WG | 942 | 146175 | 769 | - | Turb. | 942 | |
| 1920 | Saint Cyrille | 3875 | WG | 936 | France | 414 | - | T3Cy. | 936 | oilfired |
| 1920 | City of Glasgow | 5321 | WG | 897 | 143700 | 632 | - | Turb. | 897 | |
| 1920 | City of Adelaide | 6588 | EG | 939 | 143683 | 800 | - | Turb. | 939 | |
| 1921 | Nalgora | 6579 | EG | 946 | 146303 | 770 | - | Turb. | 946 | |
| 1921 | not known | | CHF | 115 | France | | 1550 | T3Cy. | 261 | CASTINGS SENT. |
| 1921 | Siantar | 8439 | EG | 943 | Holland | 800 | - | Turb. | 943 | |
| 1921 | City of Yokohama | 7341 | WG | 891 | 145918 | 917 | - | Turb. | 891 | |
| 1921 | Havre Oil Depot | | - | | | | | | 263 | Oil Pumping set: Non-marine |
| 1921 | Queenswood /Araiiz | | NW | 125 | 147776 | 339 | - | T3Cy. | 264 | |

| YEAR | SHIP | GRT | BLDR | YARD No. | OFF. No. | NHP | IHP | TYPE | ENG. No. | REMARKS |
|---|---|---|---|---|---|---|---|---|---|---|
| 1921 | not known | | CHF | 113 | France | | 1550 | T3Cy. | 259 | CASTINGS SENT. |
| 1921 | Artza-Mendi | 4597 | EU | 51 | Spain | 489 | 1450 | T3Cy. | 262 | Tanker. |
| 1921 | not known | | CHF | 114 | France | | 1550 | T3Cy. | 260 | CASTINGS SENT. |
| 1921 | Nagina | 6551 | WG | 941 | 144267 | 769 | - | Turb. | 941 | |
| 1921 | City of Simla | 9488 | WG | 883 | 146273 | 1243 | - | Turb. | 883 | Twin Screw |
| 1921 | City of Evansville | 6558 | WG | 919 | 145980 | 617 | 4340 | T3Cy. | 919 | |
| 1922 | Stad Haarlem / Atacama | 3235 | WG | 940 | Holland | 414 | - | T3Cy. | 940 | laid down as "St.Denis" (canc) |
| 1922 | Modjokerto | 8396 | EG | 948 | Holland | 800 | 5160 | Turb. | 948 | |
| 1922 | City of Singapore | 6567 | WG | 920 | 147197 | 617 | 4340 | T3Cy. | 920 | |
| 1922 | Naringa | 6607 | EG | 959 | 146333 | 770 | 4840 | Turb. | 959 | Parsons-type. 11.8 knots |
| 1922 | Colorado/City of Osaka | 6613 | WG | 945 | 147063 | 770 | 4500 | Turb. | 945 | |
| 1923 | Bluestone | 1367 | SHWR | 1215 | 147523 | 120 | - | T3Cy. | 256 ? | Engine probably 'surplus'. |
| 1923 | City of Athens | 6562 | WG | 947 | 147227 | 666 | - | T3Cy. | 947 | |
| 1923 | Knaresboro/City of W * | 7247 | EG | 958 | 147560 | 664 | - | T3Cy. | 958 | * Windsor. |
| 1923 | Kohistan | 4366 | WG | 952 | 147943 | 515 | - | T3Cy. | 952 | Oil fired |
| 1923 | Bardistan | 4357 | WG | 951 | 147461 | 515 | - | T3Cy. | 951 | |
| 1923 | City of Eastbourne | 5552 | WG | 944 | 147213 | 597 | - | T3Cy. | 944 | |
| 1924 | Rustington | 3728 | WG | 966 | 148519 | 332 | - | T3Cy. | 966 | |
| 1924 | Rudby | 4846 | WG | 962 | 139234 | - | - | T3Cy. | 962 | |
| 1924 | Querimba | 7769 | EG | 964 | 148548 | 923 | - | Quad. | 964 | |
| 1924 | Medjerda | 4380 | WG | 957 | 143983 | 386 | - | T3Cy. | 957 | |
| 1924 | Dewstone | 1371 | SHWR | 1247 | 147687 | - | - | T3Cy. | 257 ? | Engine built 1919: 'surplus' |
| 1924 | City of Salisbury | 5946 | WG | 955 | 147264 | 574 | - | T3Cy. | 955 | |
| 1924 | Nitedal / Cairnhill | 3909 | WG | 961 | Norway | 301 | - | T3Cy. | 961 | |
| 1924 | Soborg | 1992 | WG | 956 | Denmark | 194 | 1200 | T3Cy. | 956 | |
| 1924 | Karetu | 3210 | WG | 950 | 121339 | 414 | - | T3Cy. | 950 | probably "St.Edouard" (canc.) |
| 1924 | City of Bedford | 6407 | EG | 960 | 147284 | 728 | - | Quad. | 960 | |
| 1924 | Domira | 3854 | WG | 949 | 147911 | 354 | - | T3Cy. | 949 | 6500 DWT |
| 1924 | Merioneth / Aberdare | 4600 | WG | 954 | 148272 | 436 | - | T3Cy. | 954 | |
| 1924 | Ruperra | 4548 | WG | 965 | 148280 | 423 | - | T3Cy. | 965 | |
| 1925 | Kartigi | 2347 | WG | 974 | 151503 | 274 | - | T3Cy. | 974 | |
| 1925 | Ainderby | 4860 | WG | 973 | 139237 | 439 | - | T3Cy. | 973 | |
| 1925 | Ingola | 4245 | WG | 953 | 147950 | 332 | - | T3Cy. | 953 | 6500 DWT |
| 1925 | City of Leicester | 3351 | WG | 977 | 147349 | 389 | - | T3Cy. | 977 | |
| 1925 | Kaponga | 2346 | WG | 976 | 151508 | 274 | - | T3Cy. | 976 | |

| YEAR | SHIP | GRT | BLDR | YARD No. | OFF. No. | NHP | IHP | TYPE | ENG. NO. | REMARKS |
|---|---|---|---|---|---|---|---|---|---|---|
| 1925 | Kiwitea | 2343 | WG | 975 | 151507 | 274 | - | T3Cy. | 975 | |
| 1925 | City of Delhi | 7606 | EG | 969 | 148871 | 720 | - | Quad. | 969 | plus Exh. Turbine. |
| 1925 | City of Kimberley | 6204 | WG | 967 | 148579 | 592 | - | T3Cy. | 967 | |
| 1925 | Platon | 4561 | EG | 971 | France | 439 | - | T3Cy. | 971 | |
| 1925 | Tresillian | 4743 | WG | 968 | 148685 | 467 | - | T3Cy. | 968 | |
| 1925 | Queda | 7766 | WG | 963 | 148518 | 933 | - | Quad. | 963 | |
| 1925 | Quiloa | 7664 | WG | 970 | 148695 | 934 | - | Quad. | 970 | |
| 1925 | Solon | 4561 | EG | 972 | France | 467 | - | T3Cy. | 972 | |
| 1926 | City of Bath | 5000 | WG | 978 | 147370 | - | 2947 | Quad. | 978 | |
| 1926 | Firby | 4868 | WG | 979 | 139238 | 439 | - | T3Cy. | 979 | |
| 1926 | Otterpool | 4867 | WG | 980 | 139239 | 439 | - | T3Cy. | 980 | |
| 1927 | Hartbridge | 5185 | WG | 983 | 139242 | 472 | - | T3Cy. | 983 | |
| 1927 | Umberleigh | 4824 | WG | 992 | 149912 | 467 | - | T3Cy. | 992 | |
| 1927 | Ullapool | 4891 | WG | 995 | 139248 | 505 | - | T3Cy. | 995 | |
| 1927 | Leeds City | 4749 | EG | 990 | 148831 | 339 | - | T3Cy. | 990 | LR(37) 339NHP |
| 1927 | Mansepool | 4894 | WG | 996 | 139250 | 439 | - | T3Cy. | 996 | |
| 1927 | Troutpool | 4886 | WG | 986 | 139243 | 439 | - | T3Cy. | 986 | |
| 1927 | Rockpool | 5006 | WG | 993 | 139247 | 439 | - | T3Cy. | 993 | |
| 1927 | not known | | HL | n.k. | | | | T3Cy. | 266 | SENT TO BUILDERS. |
| 1927 | Ramillies | 4553 | EG | 989 | 148293 | 423 | - | T3Cy. | 989 | |
| 1927 | City of Canberra | 7645 | WG | 985 | 149651 | - | 4723 | Quad. | 985 | |
| 1927 | Quebec City | 4654 | EG | 991 | 148833 | 484 | - | T3Cy. | 991 | LR(37) 339NHP |
| 1927 | not known | | ? | n.k. | | | | T3Cy. | 265 | SENT TO GEO. CLARK. |
| 1927 | Myson | 4601 | WG | 988 | France | - | 2015 | T3Cy. | 988 | |
| 1927 | Criton | 4601 | WG | 984 | France | 439 | 2015 | T3Cy. | 984 | |
| 1927 | Romanby | 4887 | WG | 987 | 139244 | 439 | - | T3Cy. | 987 | |
| 1927 | Warlaby | 4876 | WG | 981 | 139241 | 439 | - | T3Cy. | 981 | |
| 1927 | Arabistan/Bandar Shahp | 5235 | WG | 982 | 149811 | 590 | - | T3Cy. | 982 | |
| 1927 | Parracombe | 4698 | WG | 998 | 149975 | 476 | - | T3Cy. | 998 | |
| 1928 | Alphacca | 5546 | EG | 1004 | Holland | - | 3186 | T3Cy. | 1004 | |
| 1928 | Alpherat | 5548 | EG | 1005 | Holland | - | 3182 | T3Cy. | 1005 | |
| 1928 | Nohata | 4817 | EG | 994 | 149988 | 494 | - | T3Cy. | 994 | |
| 1928 | King City | 4743 | EG | 1002 | 148835 | 484 | - | T3Cy. | 1002 | LR(37) 339NHP Oilfired |
| 1928 | Carperby | 4890 | WG | 1007 | 139257 | 505 | - | T3Cy. | 1007 | |
| 1928 | Lackenby | 5112 | WG | 1008 | 139260 | 505 | - | T3Cy. | 1008 | |

| YEAR | SHIP | GRT | BLDR | YARD No. | OFF. No. | NHP | IHP | TYPE | ENG. No. | REMARKS |
|---|---|---|---|---|---|---|---|---|---|---|
| 1928 | Thirlby | 4888 | EG | 997 | 139251 | 505 | - | T3Cy. | 997 | |
| 1928 | Coryton | 4553 | WG | 1009 | 148303 | 423 | - | T3Cy. | 1009 | |
| 1928 | Strabon | 4617 | WG | 1010 | France | 439 | - | T3Cy. | 1010 | |
| 1928 | Alona-Mendi | 1597 | WG | 1013 | Spain | 291 | - | T3Cy. | 1013 | |
| 1928 | Egglestone / Peleus | 4694 | WG | 999 | 139253 | 467 | - | T3Cy. | 999 | |
| 1928 | Rio Diamante | 4641 | WG | 1003 | 160418 | 394 | 2465 | Quad. | 1003 | Blister type. 8690 DWT |
| 1928 | Bradlyne | 4740 | WG | 1001 | 148834 | 484 | - | T3Cy. | 1001 | oilfired |
| 1928 | Aralar-Mendi | 1597 | WG | 1012 | Spain | 291 | - | T3Cy. | 1012 | |
| 1928 | Hindpool | 4897 | WG | 1006 | 139256 | 505 | - | T3Cy. | 1006 | |
| 1929 | Brookwood | 5082 | WG | 1017 | 160724 | 500 | - | T3Cy. | 1017 | Exh.Turb & steam compressor |
| 1929 | Lady Plymouth | 4732 | EG | 1031 | 148317 | 459 | - | T3Cy. | 1031 | |
| 1929 | Haxby | 5207 | WG | 1016 | 160760 | 529 | - | T3Cy. | 1016 | |
| 1929 | Tacoma City | 4748 | EG | 1020 | 148840 | 339 | - | T3Cy. | 1020 | LR(37) 339NHP |
| 1929 | Theofano | 4720 | WG | 1011 | Greece | 438 | - | T3Cy. | 1011 | |
| 1929 | Andutz-Mendi | 1808 | WG | 1014 | Spain | 291 | - | T3Cy. | 1014 | |
| 1929 | Bradglen | 5082 | WG | 1023 | 161616 | 500 | - | Quad. | 1023 | LR(37) 258NHP |
| 1929 | Glendene | 4412 | EG | 1029 | 161015 | 360 | - | T3Cy. | 1029 | TD |
| 1929 | Victoria City | 4740 | EG | 1022 | 161614 | 258 | - | Quad. | 1022 | |
| 1929 | Dunelmia | 5533 | WG | 1028 | 160763 | 484 | - | T3Cy. | 1028 | TD |
| 1929 | Yearby | 5666 | WG | 1027 | 160764 | 529 | - | T3Cy. | 1027 | |
| 1929 | Swiftpool | 5205 | WG | 1026 | 160761 | 528 | - | T3Cy. | 1026 | Pulverised fuel tested. |
| 1929 | Sheaf Crown | 5077 | WG | 1025 | 161538 | 382 | - | Quad. | 1025 | |
| 1929 | Prince Rupert City | 4737 | EG | 1019 | 148839 | 500 | - | T3Cy. | 1019 | LR(37) 339NHP |
| 1929 | Veerhaven | 5291 | EG | 1032 | Holland | 463 | - | Quad. | 1032 | |
| 1929 | City of Dieppe | 7560 | WG | 1000 | 160254 | 1008 | - | Quad. | 1000 | Plus Exh.Turbine |
| 1929 | Polzella | 4751 | WG | 1024 | 148484 | 440 | - | T3Cy. | 1024 | |
| 1929 | Atxuri-Mendi | 1597 | WG | 1030 | Spain | 291 | - | T3Cy. | 1030 | |
| 1929 | Vernon City | 4738 | EG | 1021 | 161612 | 339 | - | T3Cy. | 1021 | |
| 1929 | Heronspool | 5202 | WG | 1015 | 160759 | 529 | - | T3Cy. | 1015 | |
| 1929 | New Westminster City | 4745 | EG | 1018 | 148838 | 339 | - | T3Cy. | 1018 | |
| 1930 | Welcombe | 4686 | WG | 1034 | 161383 | 421 | 2271 | Quad. | 1034 | See NDM article 26.3.1930 |
| 1930 | Flynderborg | 1999 | WG | 1044 | Denmark | 194 | 1200 | T3Cy. | 1044 | |
| 1930 | Somersby | 5186 | WG | 1043 | 160769 | 484 | - | T3Cy. | 1043 | LR(37) 369NHP |
| 1930 | Nordborg | 1999 | WG | 1040 | Denmark | 194 | 1200 | T3Cy. | 1040 | |
| 1930 | Aithis | 4108 | EG | 1036 | Greece | 435 | - | T3Cy. | 1036 | |

| YEAR | SHIP | GRT | BLDR | YARD No. | OFF. No. | NHP | IHP | TYPE | ENG. No. | REMARKS |
|------|------|-----|------|----------|----------|-----|-----|------|----------|---------|
| 1930 | Harperley | 4585 | WG | 1041 | 161459 | 435 | - | T3Cy. | 1041 | |
| 1930 | Dellshaven | 5287 | EG | 1033 | Holland | 463 | - | Quad. | 1033 | |
| 1930 | Deerpool | 5200 | WG | 1042 | 160768 | 484 | - | T3Cy. | 1042 | LR(37) 369NHP |
| 1930 | Clumberhall | 5483 | WG | 1039 | 160767 | 442 | - | Quad. | 1039 | |
| 1930 | Josephine Gray | 1964 | WG | 1045 | 160770 | 229 | 1000 | T3Cy. | 1045 | TD: ordered as Livingstone III |
| 1930 | Margam Abbey / Notou | 2383 | WG | 1038 | 162086 | 234 | - | T3Cy. | 1038 | LR(37) 275NHP |
| 1930 | Bradburn | 5521 | WG | 1035 | 161617 | 529 | - | Quad. | 1035 | LR(37) 258NHP |
| 1930 | Thetis | 4123 | EG | 1037 | Greece | 435 | - | T3Cy. | 1037 | |
| 1931 | Challenger HMS | | NDC | n.k. | Admiralty | | | T3Cy. | 267 | SENT TO CHATHAM. |
| 1931 | Edenside | | ? | n.k. | —— | | | T3Cy. | 267 | Engines supplied. |
| 1932 | Domby | 5605 | WG | 1050 | 160771 | 484 | - | T3Cy. | 1050 | LR(37) 369NHP |
| 1932 | Kepwickhall | 4830 | WG | 1052 | 160773 | 468 | - | Quad. | 1052 | First 'Quadropod' engine. |
| 1932 | Hartismere | 5498 | WG | 1055 | 163309 | 470 | 2100 | Quad. | 1055 | 9150 DWT. "Quadropod" engine. |
| 1932 | Siltonhall | 4816 | WG | 1053 | 160774 | 468 | - | Quad. | 1053 | 2nd 'Quadropod' engine. |
| 1932 | Hartlepool | 5599 | WG | 1054 | 162759 | 470 | 2100 | Quad. | 1054 | 9150 DWT. "Quadropod" engine. |
| 1932 | B.O.Davies | 172 | WG | 1058 | 160736 | 64 | - | T3Cy. | 1058 | Pilot Cutter. |
| 1932 | Hartington | 5495 | WG | 1051 | 162716 | 470 | 2100 | Quad. | 1051 | 9150 DWT. "Quadropod" engine. |
| 1934 | Tattershall Castle | 556 | WG | 1059 | 162888 | 194 | 1200 | T3Cy. | 1059 | Paddle. |
| 1934 | Wingfield Castle | 556 | WG | 1060 | 162889 | 194 | 1200 | T3Cy. | 1060 | Paddle. Now @ Hpl restored. |
| 1935 | Clearpool | 5404 | WG | 1057 | 162107 | - | 2200 | Turb. | 1057 | IHP=Shaft HP. |
| 1935 | Boltonhall | 4738 | WG | 1056 | 160775 | 468 | - | Quad. | 1056 | "Quadropod" engine. See 1943. |
| 1936 | Cressdene | 4270 | WG | 1061 | 164608 | 289 | - | T3Cy. | 1061 | TD: £61,000 Scrap & Build Loan |
| 1936 | Hawnby | 5404 | WG | 1063 | 162111 | - | 2200 | Turb. | 1063 | IHP=Shaft HP. |
| 1936 | Melrose Abbey | 2472 | WG | 1066 | 162109 | 269 | - | T3Cy. | 1066 | LR(37) 234NHP |
| 1936 | Germanic | 5351 | WG | 1067 | 164969 | 460 | - | T3Cy. | 1067 | |
| 1936 | Eugenie Livanos | 4816 | WG | 1062 | Greece | 460 | - | T3Cy. | 1062 | |
| 1936 | Athenic | 5350 | WG | 1070 | 164995 | 460 | - | T3Cy. | 1070 | |
| 1936 | Oakdene | 4255 | WG | 1071 | 165350 | 289 | - | T3Cy. | 1071 | TD : Drop valves. |
| 1936 | Athina Livanos | 4824 | WG | 1065 | Greece | 460 | - | T3Cy. | 1065 | |
| 1936 | Tordene | 4254 | WG | 1064 | 164362 | 289 | - | T3Cy. | 1064 | TD |
| 1937 | Lindenhall | 5247 | WG | 1076 | 160778 | 542 | - | T3Cy. | 1076 | plus Exh. Turbine |
| 1937 | Malvernian | 3132 | WG | 1072 | 164324 | 606 | - | T3Cy. | 1072 | plus Exh. Turbine |
| 1937 | Felldene | 4332 | WG | 1074 | 165434 | 289 | 1290 | T3Cy. | 1074 | TD: Drop valves: 9.75 knots. |
| 1937 | Evi Livanos | 4839 | WG | 1081 | Greece | 460 | - | T3Cy. | 1081 | |
| 1937 | Hazard HMS | 1350D | WG | 1068 | Admiralty | - | 1750 | Turb. | 1068 | IHP=Shaft HP.  Survey vessel. |

| YEAR | SHIP | GRT | BLDR | YARD No. | OFF. No. | NHP | IHP | TYPE | ENG. No. | REMARKS |
|---|---|---|---|---|---|---|---|---|---|---|
| 1937 | Danby | 4281 | WG | 1077 | 160776 | 289 | - | T3Cy. | 1077 | |
| 1937 | Belgravian | 3136 | WG | 1073 | 164337 | 606 | - | T3Cy. | 1073 | plus Exh. Turbine |
| 1937 | Theolano Livanos | 6636 | WG | 1075 | Greece | 460 | - | T3Cy. | 1075 | |
| 1937 | G.S.Livanos | 4835 | WG | 1078 | Greece | 460 | - | T3Cy. | 1078 | |
| 1937 | Gleaner HMS | 1350D | WG | 1069 | Admiralty | - | 1750 | Turb. | 1069 | IHP=Shaft HP. Survey vessel. |
| 1938 | Mary Livanos | 4771 | WG | 1088 | Greece | 463 | - | T3Cy. | 1088 | |
| 1938 | Margam Abbey | 2470 | WG | 1085 | 162127 | 269 | 900 | T3Cy. | 1085 | |
| 1938 | Indora | 6622 | WG | 1080 | 166382 | 592 | - | T3Cy. | 1080 | plus Exh. Turbine |
| 1938 | Palermo | 2838 | WG | 1087 | 165710 | 492 | - | T3Cy. | 1087 | |
| 1938 | Ilinda / Zhan Dou 34 | 6648 | WG | 1079 | 166236 | 592 | 3070 | T3Cy. | 1079 | 12k. Exh. Turbine fitted. |
| 1938 | Ionian | 3114 | WG | 1082 | 166236 | 606 | - | T3Cy. | 1082 | |
| 1938 | George M. Livanos | 5481 | WG | 1089 | Greece | 492 | - | T3Cy. | 1089 | |
| 1938 | Fauzon | 4319 | WG | 1092 | France | 553 | - | T3Cy. | 1092 | |
| 1938 | Arijon | 4374 | WG | 1086 | France | 553 | 2155 | T3Cy. | 1086 | |
| 1938 | Corinthian | 3198 | WG | 1083 | 166246 | 606 | - | T3Cy. | 1083 | plus Exh. Turbine. |
| 1938 | Michael Livanos | 4773 | WG | 1084 | Greece | 463 | - | T3Cy. | 1084 | |
| 1939 | Tintern Abbey | 2479 | WG | 1090 | 162131 | 269 | - | T3Cy. | 1090 | |
| 1939 | Chios | 5643 | WG | 1091 | Greece | 492 | - | T3Cy. | 1091 | |
| 1939 | Vasco | 2829 | WG | 1096 | 167078 | 460 | - | T3Cy. | 1096 | |
| 1939 | Nicholas D. L. | 5486 | WG | 1093 | Greece | 492 | - | T3Cy. | 1093 | |
| 1939 | Atlantic | 5439 | WG | 1094 | 167069 | 461 | - | T3Cy. | 1094 | |
| 1939 | Elmdene | 4856 | WG | 1095 | 167371 | 397 | | T3Cy. | 1095 | TD: 1939 "Scrap & Build" |
| 1939 | not known | | ? | n.k. | Spain ? | | | T3Cy. | 268 | CASTINGS;shipped per "Bidassoa" |
| 1940 | Duke of Sparta/Aquila | 5330 | WG | 1104 | 168027 | 492 | - | T3Cy. | 1104 | 1939 "Scrap & Build" |
| 1940 | Empire Strait | 2841 | WG | 1112 | 160789 | 255 | - | T3Cy. | 1112 | |
| 1940 | Ismailia | 6806 | WG | 1105 | 168047 | 669 | - | T3Cy. | 1105 | |
| 1940 | Florian | 3137 | WG | 1099 | 166292 | 606 | 3000 | T3Cy. | 1099 | 13.5 knots |
| 1940 | Ottinge | 2818 | WG | 1098 | 167799 | 255 | - | T3Cy. | 1098 | |
| 1940 | Itaura | 6802 | WG | 1103 | 168012 | 669 | - | T3Cy. | 1103 | plus Exh. Turbine |
| 1940 | not known | | SH | n.k. | —— | | | T3Cy. | 269 | CASTINGS & AUX. SENT TO BLDRS. |
| 1940 | Empire Bay | 2824 | WG | 1107 | 160786 | 255 | - | T3Cy. | 1107 | |
| 1940 | Ruckinge | 2869 | WG | 1097 | 167796 | 255 | - | T3Cy. | 1097 | |
| 1940 | Ikauna | 6801 | WG | 1106 | 168072 | 669 | - | T3Cy. | 1106 | |
| 1940 | Itola | 6812 | WG | 1102 | 167619 | 669 | - | T3Cy. | 1102 | |
| 1940 | Industria | 4734 | WG | 1100 | 160782 | 460 | - | T3Cy. | 1100 | TD: 1939 "Scrap & Build" |

| YEAR | SHIP | GRT | BLDR | YARD No. | OFF. No. | NHP | IHP | TYPE | ENG. No. | REMARKS |
|---|---|---|---|---|---|---|---|---|---|---|
| 1940 | Empire Lough | 2824 | WG | 1108 | 160778 | 255 | - | T3Cy. | 1108 | |
| 1940 | Cape Breton | 6044 | WG | 1101 | 167607 | 461 | - | T3Cy. | 1101 | |
| 1941 | Empire Wolfe | 2888 | WG | 1119 | 168930 | 269 | - | T3Cy. | 1119 | |
| 1941 | Empire Hurst | 2852 | WG | 1116 | 160795 | 255 | - | T3Cy. | 1116 | |
| 1941 | Empire Newcomen | 2840 | WG | 1120 | 168932 | 269 | - | T3Cy. | 1120 | |
| 1941 | Empire Sedge | 2773 | WG | 1117 | 168928 | 255 | - | T3Cy. | 1117 | |
| 1941 | Empire Cabot | 6715 | WG | 1118 | 168929 | 460 | - | T3Cy. | 1118 | |
| 1941 | Empire Ocean | 6765 | WG | 1110 | 160794 | 461 | - | T3Cy. | 1110 | |
| 1941 | Empire Sunbeam | 6743 | WG | 1111 | 160792 | 460 | - | T3Cy. | 1111 | |
| 1941 | Empire Parsons | 6742 | WG | 1121 | 168931 | 460 | - | T3Cy. | 1121 | |
| 1941 | Empire Marlowe | 6768 | WG | 1122 | 168933 | 505 | - | T3Cy. | 1122 | |
| 1941 | Empire Lake | 2852 | WG | 1114 | 160791 | 255 | - | T3Cy. | 1114 | |
| 1941 | Empire Brook | 2866 | WG | 1115 | 160793 | 255 | - | T3Cy. | 1115 | |
| 1941 | Empire Knoll | 2824 | WG | 1113 | 160790 | 255 | - | T3Cy. | 1113 | |
| 1941 | Empire Darwin | 6782 | WG | 1109 | 168927 | 417 | - | T3Cy. | 1109 | |
| 1942 | Empire Arnold | 7045 | WG | 1127 | 168939 | 510 | - | T3Cy. | 1127 | |
| 1942 | Empire Clarion | 7019 | WG | 1133 | 168944 | 510 | - | T3Cy. | 1133 | |
| 1942 | Empire Carey | 2830 | WG | 1134 | 168934 | 269 | - | T3Cy. | 1134 | |
| 1942 | Nordelfinge | 2873 | WG | 1139 | 168637 | 269 | - | T3Cy. | 1139 | |
| 1942 | Empire Pilgrim | 2828 | WG | 1126 | 168935 | 269 | - | T3Cy. | 1126 | |
| 1942 | Empire Caxton | 2873 | WG | 1131 | 168940 | 269 | - | T3Cy. | 1131 | |
| 1942 | Empire Record | 2967 | WG | 1143 | 168950 | 269 | - | T3Cy. | 1143 | |
| 1942 | Empire Tennyson | 2880 | WG | 1129 | 168936 | 269 | - | T3Cy. | 1129 | |
| 1942 | Empire Purcell | 7049 | WG | 1124 | 168937 | 510 | - | T3Cy. | 1124 | |
| 1942 | Empire Builder /Tobruk | 7049 | WG | 1123 | Poland | 510 | - | T3Cy. | 1123 | |
| 1942 | Empire Patriot | 2881 | WG | 1136 | 168943 | 269 | - | T3Cy. | 1136 | |
| 1942 | Empire Lorenzo | 2865 | WG | 1140 | 168948 | 269 | - | T3Cy. | 1140 | |
| 1942 | Empire Elgar | 2932 | WG | 1130 | 168938 | 269 | - | T3Cy. | 1130 | |
| 1942 | Empire Cato | 7025 | WG | 1138 | 168949 | 510 | - | T3Cy. | 1138 | |
| 1942 | Empire Centaur | 7075 | WG | 1134 | 168946 | 510 | - | T3Cy. | 1134 | |
| 1942 | Empire Gareth | 2856 | WG | 1132 | 168942 | 269 | - | T3Cy. | 1132 | |
| 1942 | Empire Lionel | 7043 | WG | 1128 | 168941 | 510 | - | T3Cy. | 1128 | |
| 1942 | Empire Boswell | 2898 | WG | 1135 | 168945 | 269 | - | T3Cy. | 1135 | |
| 1943 | Empire Buttress | 2936 | WG | 1150 | 168959 | 281 | - | T3Cy. | 1150 | |
| 1943 | Empire Seaman | 2915 | WG | 1156 | 168963 | 281 | - | T3Cy. | 1156 | |

| YEAR | SHIP | GRT | BLDR | YARD No. | OFF. No. | NHP | IHP | TYPE | ENG. No. | REMARKS |
|---|---|---|---|---|---|---|---|---|---|---|
| 1943 | Empire Nigel | 7052 | WG | 1152 | 168962 | 510 | - | T3Cy. | 1152 | |
| 1943 | Empire Mountain | 2906 | WG | 1149 | 168957 | 281 | - | T3Cy. | 1149 | |
| 1943 | Boltonhall (Gray 1935) | 4824 | WG | 1056 | 160775 | 458 | - | T3Cy. | 270 ? | New engine '43. No superheat. |
| 1943 | Empire Gulliver | 2905 | WG | 1153 | 168960 | 281 | - | T3Cy. | 1153 | |
| 1943 | Empire Candida | 2974 | WG | 1144 | 168951 | 269 | - | T3Cy. | 1144 | |
| 1943 | Empire Mortimer | 7051 | WG | 1141 | 168952 | 510 | - | T3Cy. | 1141 | |
| 1943 | Empire Harmony | 2974 | WG | 1145 | 168953 | 269 | - | T3Cy. | 1145 | |
| 1943 | Empire Rival/Amberton | 6721 | WG | 1151 | 168961 | 510 | - | T3Cy. | 1151 | |
| 1943 | Empire Ransom | 2905 | WG | 1157 | 168964 | 281 | - | T3Cy. | 1157 | |
| 1943 | Empire Prowess | 7060 | WG | 1142 | 168954 | 510 | - | T3Cy. | 1142 | |
| 1943 | Empire Peak | 6994 | WG | 1148 | 168958 | 510 | - | T3Cy. | 1148 | |
| 1943 | Empire Ploughman | 7049 | WG | 1154 | 168965 | 510 | - | T3Cy. | 1154 | |
| 1943 | Empire Stalwart | 7066 | WG | 1147 | 168956 | 510 | - | T3Cy. | 1147 | |
| 1943 | Empire Valour | 2908 | WG | 1146 | 168955 | 269 | - | T3Cy. | 1146 | |
| 1943 | Empire Lankester | 7051 | WG | 1161 | 180071 | 510 | - | T3Cy. | 1161 | |
| 1944 | Empire Bermuda/Hewsang | 3541 | WG | 1173 | 180078 | 299 | - | T3Cy. | 1173 | |
| 1944 | Empire Sedley | 2905 | WG | 1163 | 180069 | 281 | - | T3Cy. | 1163 | |
| 1944 | Empire Labrador | 3539 | WG | 1170 | 180077 | 299 | - | T3Cy. | 1170 | |
| 1944 | Empire Osborne | 2922 | WG | 1164 | 180070 | 281 | - | T3Cy. | 1164 | |
| 1944 | Empire Irving | 7081 | WG | 1162 | 180073 | 510 | - | T3Cy. | 1162 | |
| 1944 | TID 110 / Taywood Tid | 54 | RDU | T.531 | 180301 | 36.4 | 220 | C2Cy. | 288 ? | 140RPM service.  CMEW Propeller |
| 1944 | Empire Newfoundland | 3539 | WG | 1169 | 180076 | 299 | - | T3Cy. | 1169 | |
| 1944 | Empire Perlis | 3541 | WG | 1168 | 180074 | 299 | - | T3Cy. | 1168 | |
| 1944 | Empire Malta | 3541 | WG | 1167 | 180072 | 299 | - | T3Cy. | 1167 | |
| 1944 | Empire Harcourt | 2902 | WG | 1160 | 180068 | 281 | - | T3Cy. | 1160 | |
| 1944 | Empire Accra/Dallas C. | 7073 | WG | 1158 | 165866 | 510 | - | T3Cy. | 1158 | later 'Dallas City' |
| 1944 | Empire Beaconsfield | 2865 | WG | 1159 | 180066 | 281 | - | T3Cy. | 1159 | |
| 1945 | Empire Dunnet | 7372 | WG | 1177 | 180086 | 510 | - | T3Cy. | 1177 | |
| 1945 | Cuillin Sound | 7340 | WG | 1171 | Admiralty | 541 | - | T3Cy. | 1171 | later "James Clunie"(48) |
| 1945 | Empire Takoradi | 7024 | WG | 1172 | 180080 | 510 | - | T3Cy. | 1172 | |
| 1945 | Empire Aldgate | 3485 | WG | 1180 | 180083 | 281 | - | T3Cy. | 1180 | |
| 1945 | Cattaro | 2885 | WG | 1183 | 180460 | 466 | - | T3Cy. | 1183 | |
| 1945 | Empire Southwark | 3486 | WG | 1181 | 180085 | 281 | - | T3Cy. | 1181 | |
| 1945 | Foochow | 3394 | WG | 1185 | 180778 | 444 | - | T3Cy. | 1185 | Poppet valve engine. |
| 1945 | Empire Caicos | 3549 | WG | 1179 | 180082 | 299 | - | T3Cy. | 1179 | |

| YEAR | SHIP | GRT | BLDR | YARD No. | OFF. No. | NHP | IHP | TYPE | ENG. No. | REMARKS |
|---|---|---|---|---|---|---|---|---|---|---|
| 1945 | Pachumba | 7073 | WG | 1175 | 180562 | 510 | - | T3Cy. | 1175 | |
| 1945 | Empire Barbados | 3549 | WG | 1178 | 180081 | 299 | - | T3Cy. | 1178 | |
| 1945 | Empire Eddystone | 7141 | WG | 1176 | 180084 | 510 | - | T3Cy. | 1176 | |
| 1945 | Empire Jamaica | 3586 | WG | 1174 | 180079 | 299 | - | T3Cy. | 1174 | |
| 1946 | Rinaldo | 4119 | WG | 1188 | 181279 | 619 | - | T3Cy. | 1188 | |
| 1946 | Empire Gower / Rogate | 2849 | WG | 1184 | 180087 | 281 | - | T3Cy. | 1184 | |
| 1946 | Urlana | 6835 | WG | 1193 | 180860 | 843 | - | T3Cy. | 1193 | L.P.Turb by Swan Hunter |
| 1946 | Fukien | 3394 | WG | 1187 | 180801 | 444 | - | T3Cy. | 1187 | Poppet valve engine. |
| 1946 | Umaria | 6835 | WG | 1194 | 180962 | 843 | - | T3Cy. | 1194 | plus Exh. Turbine. |
| 1946 | TID 168 / Lea | 54 | RDU | T.629 | 181263 | 36.4 | 220 | C2Cy. | 289 ? | 140 RPM service |
| 1946 | Ariosto | 2208 | WG | 1189 | 181264 | 435 | - | T3Cy. | 1189 | Exh. Turb. 13 knots |
| 1946 | Fengtien | 3394 | WG | 1186 | 180819 | 444 | - | T3Cy. | 1186 | Poppet valve engine. |
| 1947 | Malmo | 1799 | WG | 1191 | 181276 | 435 | - | T3Cy. | 1191 | plus Exh. Turbine |
| 1947 | Tinto | 1795 | HR | 355 | 181292 | 428 | - | T3Cy. | 290 | plus Exh. Turbine |
| 1947 | Livorno | 2957 | WG | 1192 | 181285 | 620 | - | T3Cy. | 1192 | |
| 1947 | Mardene | 4750 | WG | 1205 | 181602 | 547 | - | T3Cy. | 1205 | TD |
| 1947 | Albano | 2239 | WG | 1190 | 181291 | 442 | - | T3Cy. | 1190 | Exh. Turb. 13 knots |
| 1947 | Riodene / Silvertarn | 4860 | WG | 1197 | 181576 | 547 | - | T3Cy. | 1197 | TD: 10+k on 18.75 T oil. |
| 1947 | Anglian | 2219 | WG | 1204 | 181086 | 442 | - | T3Cy. | 1204 | plus Exh. Turbine |
| 1947 | Truro | 1795 | HR | 356 | 181297 | 428 | - | T3Cy. | 291 | plus Exh. Turbine |
| 1947 | Francisco Matarazzo | 4904 | WG | 1208 | Brazil | 547 | 2500 | T3Cy. | 1208 | TD |
| 1947 | Vernon | 4518 | WG | 1206 | France | 802 | - | Turb. | 1206 | |
| 1947 | Silvio | 1798 | HR | 358 | 181321 | 428 | - | T3Cy. | 293 | |
| 1947 | Chinon | 4518 | WG | 1207 | France | 802 | - | Turb. | 1207 | |
| 1947 | Bravo | 1797 | HR | 357 | 181306 | 428 | - | T3Cy. | 292 | plus Exh. turbine. |
| 1948 | Irish Rose | 1923 | WG | 1222 | Eire | - | 1785 | T3Cy. | 1222 | |
| 1948 | Boca Maule | 2312 | WG | 1213 | Chile | 656 | 2600 | T3Cy. | 1213 | TD |
| 1948 | Avondene | 4968 | WG | 1220 | 182885 | - | 1950 | T3Cy. | 1220 | TD |
| 1948 | Irish Willow | 1767 | WG | 1223 | Eire | - | 1785 | T3Cy. | 1223 | |
| 1948 | Erik Banck / Armant | 2312 | WG | 1215 | Norway | 499 | 1800 | T3Cy. | 1215 | |
| 1948 | E.Matarazzo /Nowrooz | 4911 | WG | 1210 | Hongkong | 547 | - | T3Cy. | 1210 | TD |
| 1948 | A.J.Falkland | 3246 | WG | 1217 | Norway | 499 | 1800 | T3Cy. | 1217 | |
| 1949 | Mary | 5841 | WG | 1228 | Greece | 668 | 2540 | T3Cy. | 1228 | |
| 1949 | Dona Isidora | 4093 | WG | 1225 | Chile | 441 | 2200 | T3Cy. | 1225 | TD |
| 1949 | Stratidore | 4786 | WG | 1229 | 183057 | 550 | 1950 | T3Cy. | 1229 | |

| YEAR | SHIP | GRT | BLDR | YARD No. | OFF. No. | NHP | IHP | TYPE | ENG. No. | REMARKS |
|------|------|-----|------|----------|----------|-----|-----|------|----------|---------|
| 1949 | Irish Cedar | 5627 | WG | 1219 | Eire | - | 3050 | T3Cy. | 1219 | |
| 1949 | Irish Plane | 5368 | WG | 1232 | Eire | - | 3050 | T3Cy. | 1232 | |
| 1949 | Tauri | 2334 | WG | 1224 | Sweden | 499 | 1995 | T3Cy. | 1224 | |
| 1950 | Irish Hazel | 5366 | WG | 1233 | Eire | - | 3050 | T3Cy. | 1233 | |
| 1950 | Spigerborg | 2276 | WG | 1234 | Denmark | - | 2154 | Motor | 1234 | IHP=Brake HP: 1st Gray-Polar. |
| 1950 | Valborg Nielsen/Avare | 2668 | WG | 1235 | Denmark | 501 | 2500 | T3Cy. | 1235 | |
| 1950 | Atlantic Duchess | 8631 | WG | 1237 | Greece | 876 | 4450 | Motor | 1237 | IHP=BHP. Tanker. Gray-Polar Eng. |
| 1951 | Exedene | 5015 | WG | 1247 | 184478 | 492 | 2645 | T3Cy. | 1247 | TD: plus Exh. Turbine |
| 1951 | Maltasian | 3910 | WG | 1243 | 183790 | 590 | 2950 | T3Cy. | 1243 | plus Exh. Turbine |
| 1951 | Seawall | 5890 | WG | 1240 | 184355 | - | 2500 | T3Cy. | 1240 | |
| 1951 | Merchant Duke | 7643 | WG | 1241 | 184407 | - | 2500 | T3Cy. | 1241 | |
| 1951 | Funing / Starford | 3464 | WG | 1244 | 184314 | - | 1970 | T3Cy. | 1244 | |
| 1951 | Andalusian | 3913 | WG | 1242 | 183768 | 590 | 2950 | T3Cy. | 1242 | plus Exh. Turbine. |
| 1951 | Toto | 6752 | WG | 1246 | Chile | - | 2645 | T3Cy. | 1246 | TD |
| 1951 | Bernhard Hansson | 8739 | WG | 1239 | Norway | - | 4720 | Motor | 1239 | Tanker: Gray-Polar Diesel. |
| 1951 | Fengning / Wishlord | 3464 | WG | 1245 | 184363 | - | 1970 | T3Cy. | 1245 | |
| 1951 | Georgios | 7451 | WG | 1238 | Greece | - | 2500 | T3Cy. | 1238 | |
| 1952 | Garlinge | 2907 | WG | 1252 | 169553 | - | 1250 | T3Cy. | 1252 | |
| 1952 | Beltinge | 2979 | WG | 1251 | 169552 | - | 1250 | T3Cy. | 1251 | |
| 1952 | Evgenia | 7406 | WG | 1254 | Liberia | - | 2500 | T3Cy. | 1254 | plus Exh. Turbine. |
| 1952 | Paysandu / St. Cergue | 4933 | WG | 1250 | Swiss | - | 2025 | T3Cy. | 1250 | plus Exh. Turbine |
| 1952 | Dunelmia | 4907 | WG | 1253 | 180096 | - | 2000 | T3Cy. | 1253 | TD: plus Exh. Turbine |
| 1953 | Queensbury | 6715 | BI | 350 | 185900 | - | - | Motor | 294 | Gray-Polar diesels. |
| 1953 | Hallindene | 5026 | WG | 1259 | 184741 | - | 2000 | T3Cy. | 1259 | TD: plus Exh. Turbine. |
| 1953 | Silverburn | 5023 | WG | 1260 | 185849 | - | 2000 | T3Cy. | 1260 | plus Exh. Turbine. |
| 1953 | Irish Elm | 5820 | WG | 1261 | Eire | - | 3050 | T3Cy. | 1261 | plus Exh. Turbine |
| 1953 | Romeral | 6763 | WG | 1255 | Chile | - | 2645 | T3Cy. | 1255 | TD |
| 1953 | Aliki Livanos | 7564 | WG | 1257 | Greece | - | 3050 | T3Cy. | 1257 | plus Exh. Turbine |
| 1953 | Appledore | 5842 | WG | 1256 | 185884 | - | 3050 | T3Cy. | 1256 | |
| 1953 | Hawkinge | 2980 | WG | 1258 | 169555 | - | 1250 | T3Cy. | 1258 | |
| 1954 | Majorka | 2340 | WG | 1277 | Norway | - | 1484 | T3Cy. | 1277 | |
| 1954 | Stanpool | 7348 | WG | 1266 | 186065 | - | 2850 | T3Cy. | 1266 | |
| 1954 | Oreosa | 6856 | WG | 1263 | 186064 | - | 3650 | Motor | 1263 | IHP=BHP. Gray-Polar. |
| 1954 | Moira / Al Nasseria | 2343 | WG | 1278 | Norway | - | 1768 | T3Cy. | 1278 | 12k |
| 1954 | Orelia | 6858 | WG | 1262 | 186007 | - | 3652 | Motor | 1262 | IHP=Brake HP. Gray-Polar. |

| YEAR | SHIP | GRT | BLDR | YARD No. | OFF. No. | NHP | IHP | TYPE | ENG. No. | REMARKS |
|------|------|-----|------|----------|----------|-----|-----|------|----------|---------|
| 1954 | Ariana | 4948 | WG | 1264 | Finland | - | 2600 | T3Cy. | 1264 | plus Exh. Turbine |
| 1955 | Orepton | 6859 | WG | 1268 | 186206 | - | 3650 | Motor | 1268 | IHP=Brake HP. Gray-Polar. |
| 1955 | Oredian | 6859 | WG | 1269 | 186258 | - | 3652 | Motor | 1269 | IHP=Brake HP. Gray-Polar. |
| 1955 | Castilian | 3803 | AST | 645 | 187107 | - | - | T3Cy. | 297 | plus Exh. Turbine |
| 1955 | Anatolian | 5064 | WG | 1281 | 187117 | - | 3500 | T3Cy. | 1281 | plus Exh. Turbine |
| 1955 | Daphne | 5957 | WG | 1271 | Liberia | - | 3050 | T3Cy. | 1271 | plus Exh. Turbine |
| 1956 | Almerian | 3649 | CAL | 502 | 187148 | - | - | T3Cy. | 296 | plus Exh. Turbine |
| 1956 | Lancastrian | 4799 | WG | 1282 | 187122 | - | 3500 | T3Cy. | 1282 | plus Exh. Turbine |
| 1957 | Castledore | 7952 | WG | 1284 | 187513 | - | 3700 | T3Cy. | 1284 | plus Exh. Turbine |
| 1957 | Lucy | 7478 | WG | 1285 | Greece | - | 3700 | T3Cy. | 1285 | L.P.Turb. See 1961 N E (Motor) |
| 1958 | Rose of Lancaster | 5215 | WG | 1290 | 187174 | - | 4800 | Turb. | 1290 | IHP=Shaft HP :Sht to 810F |
| 1959 | Mary Holt | 5577 | WG | 1300 | 301319 | - | 4800 | Turb. | 1300 | Pametrada designed turbine. |
| 1959 | Dixcove | 8138 | WG | 1296 | 301309 | - | 5500 | Motor | 1296 | IHP=BHP |
| 1959 | Degema | 8153 | WG | 1295 | 301300 | - | 5500 | Motor | 1295 | IHP=BHP |
| 1960 | Mabel Warwick /Rubini | 11932 | WG | 1301 | 301070 | - | 5500 | Motor | 1301 | IHP=BHP |
| 1960 | Joya McCance | 11871 | WG | 1307 | 301246 | - | 5500 | Motor | 1307 | IHP=Brake HP. 16830DWT |
| 1961 | Irish Sycamore | 10333 | WG | 1302 | 400296 | - | 6800 | Motor | 1302 | IHP=BHP |
| 1961 | Lucy | 7478 | WG | 1285 | Greece | - | 3400 | Motor | 298 | Original T3Cy. replaced 1961. |

# APPENDIX 'B'

List of contract prices for engines and ships.

(for this information the author is indebted to the kindness of Peter Barton of Kenilworth, who extracted it from his collection of William Gray contracts).

The prices shown in the list are contract prices and may not have been what was finally the actual cost to the shipowner. The last column is for hull and machinery.

| YEAR | SHIP | No. | TYPE | NHP | IHP | No. | ENG | SHIP COST |
|------|------|-----|------|-----|-----|-----|-----|-----------|
| 1888 | Humber | 349 | T3Cy. | 250 | 1150 | 38 | £6,800 | £23,950 |
| 1888 | Duke of Cornwall | 339 | T3Cy. | 156 | 800 | 27 | £5,050 | £18,350 |
| 1888 | Lowlands | 336 | T3Cy. | 150 | 800 | 26 | £5,000 | £18,400 |
| 1888 | Marie | 345 | T3Cy. | 169 | 900 | 34 | £5,350 | £20,400 |
| 1888 | Muriel | 351 | T3Cy. | 200 | 1100 | 41 | £6,400 | £24,896 |
| 1888 | Urania | 330 | T3Cy. | 220 | 1250 | 24 | £7,000 | £24,000 |
| 1888 | Missouri | 346 | T3Cy. | 274 | 1500 | 32 | £9,200 | £34,000 |
| 1888 | Harrow | 332 | T3Cy. | 220 | 1250 | 22 | £7,250 | £26,000 |
| 1888 | Carrie | 342 | T3Cy. | 156 | 800 | 29 | £5,050 | £18,750 |
| 1888 | Kittie | 331 | T2Cy | 210 | 1100 | 25 | £6,500 | £22,575 |
| 1888 | Cranford | 341 | T3Cy. | 240 | 1250 | 30 | £7,000 | £23,824 |
| 1888 | New Borough /Pensacola | 340 | T3Cy. | 150 | 800 | 28 | £5,050 | £18,350 |
| 1888 | Egglestone Abbey | 343 | T3Cy. | 200 | 1150 | 33 | £6,800 | £24,500 |
| 1889 | Calliope | 365 | T3Cy. | 240 | 1300 | 45 | £7,400 | £27,750 |
| 1889 | Duchess of Cornwall | 356 | T3Cy. | 150 | 900 | 36 | £5,150 | £19,125 |
| 1889 | Chingford | 369 | T3Cy. | 168 | 1000 | 54 | £5,650 | £20,050 |
| 1889 | Norsa | 375 | T3Cy. | 180 | 1200 | 60 | £6,500 | £23,650 |
| 1889 | Falka | 355 | T3Cy. | 156 | 900 | 40 | £5,150 | £19,125 |
| 1889 | Mortlake | 359 | T3Cy. | 250 | 1300 | 44 | £7,250 | £26,400 |
| 1889 | Ermanarich | 364 | T3Cy. | 150 | 900 | 49 | £5,150 | £16,500 |
| 1889 | Redcar | 366 | T3Cy. | 150 | 900 | 51 | £5,150 | £19,500 |
| 1889 | Empress / Ningoote | 360 | T3Cy. | 274 | 1850 | 50 | £9,600 | n.k. |
| 1889 | Thurston | 358 | T3Cy. | 169 | 1000 | 35 | £5,605 | £19,200 |
| 1889 | Alarich | 363 | T3Cy. | 140 | 900 | 48 | £5,150 | £16,500 |
| 1889 | Geiserich/Karthago | 362 | T3Cy. | 156 | 900 | 47 | £5,150 | £16,500 |
| 1889 | Romulus | 372 | T3Cy. | 250 | 1300 | 57 | £7,750 | £28,000 |
| 1889 | Marmion | 370 | T3Cy. | 160 | 1000 | 56 | £5,650 | £20,050 |
| 1889 | Cornubia | 377 | T3Cy. | 156 | 900 | 62 | £5,400 | £20,800 |
| 1889 | Elmville | 367 | T3Cy. | 169 | 1000 | 52 | £5,605 | £20,960 |
| 1889 | Eton | 380 | T3Cy. | 240 | 1300 | 64 | £9,000 | £30,250 |
| 1889 | Theodorich | 361 | T3Cy. | 140 | 900 | 46 | £5,150 | £16,500 |
| 1889 | Garlands | 368 | T3Cy. | 165 | 1000 | 53 | £5,550 | £21,750 |
| 1889 | Ariel / Samara | 352 | T3Cy. | 240 | 1300 | 43 | £7,400 | £27,750 |
| 1889 | Remus | 373 | T3Cy. | 260 | 1300 | 58 | £7,750 | £28,000 |
| 1889 | Iona | 374 | T3Cy. | 180 | 1200 | 59 | £6,500 | £23,650 |
| 1889 | Norlands / Pena Rocias | 353 | T3Cy. | 156 | 900 | 37 | £5,150 | £19,000 |
| 1889 | Westbrook | 376 | T3Cy. | 150 | 900 | 61 | £5,350 | £20,000 |
| 1890 | Halifax City / Kestor | 391 | T3Cy. | 200 | 1200 | 72 | £7,750 | £31,500 |
| 1890 | Bussorah/Greatham | 382 | T3Cy. | 210 | 1200 | 66 | £7,550 | £27,500 |
| 1890 | Fulham | 386 | T3Cy. | 165 | 1000 | 74 | £6,225 | £26,000 |
| 1890 | Guernsey | 404 | T3Cy. | 220 | 1300 | 92 | £8,050 | £30,450 |
| 1890 | Herman Wedel Jarlsberg | 400 | T3Cy. | 240 | 1500 | 86 | £10,560 | £40,750 |
| 1890 | Armenia | 381 | T3Cy. | 200 | 1250 | 68 | £8,000 | n.k. |
| 1890 | Macduff | 403 | T3Cy. | 288 | 1300 | 90 | £10,830 | £36,880 |
| 1890 | Pocklington | 383 | T3Cy. | 130 | 800 | 69 | £5,280 | £18,000 |
| 1890 | Sestao | 395 | T3Cy. | 150 | 1000 | 79 | £6,550 | £22,300 |
| 1890 | Kingsland | 387 | T3Cy. | 200 | 1000 | 75 | £6,225 | £26,000 |
| 1890 | Oaklands | 402 | T3Cy. | 168 | 1000 | 89 | £5,500 | £22,750 |
| 1890 | Coatham | 398 | T3Cy. | 150 | 900 | 84 | £6,500 | £23,750 |
| 1890 | Frieda | 401 | T3Cy. | 207 | 1200 | 88 | £6,300 | £23,500 |
| 1890 | Ipsden | 397 | T3Cy. | 150 | 900 | 83 | £6,500 | £23,400 |
| 1890 | Calcutta City / Langoe | 390 | T3Cy. | 204 | 1200 | 91 | £7,750 | £28,000 |
| 1890 | Malvern | 393 | T3Cy. | 250 | 1300 | 73 | £7,750 | £31,500 |
| 1890 | Rangatira | 392 | T3Cy. | 450 | 2180 | 70 | £13,320 | £49,250 |

| YEAR | SHIP | No. | TYPE | NHP | IHP | No. | ENG | SHIP COST |
|------|------|-----|------|-----|-----|-----|-----|-----------|
| 1890 | Umhloti | 399 | T3Cy. | 250 | 1300 | 85 | £10,750 | £34,650 |
| 1890 | Umbilo | 379 | T3Cy. | 210 | 1250 | 65 | £8,250 | £26,000 |
| 1890 | Elloe / Konstantinos | 396 | T3Cy. | 147 | 900 | 82 | £6,500 | £23,400 |
| 1890 | Manchester | 388 | T3Cy. | 207 | 1200 | 76 | £7,450 | £29,500 |
| 1890 | Tekoa | 394 | T3Cy. | 450 | 2180 | 80 | £13,320 | £49,250 |
| 1890 | Taurus | 406 | T3Cy. | 180 | 1200 | 77 | £6,334 | £25,000 |
| 1891 | Gledhow | 409 | T3Cy. | 239 | 1300 | 97 | £7,750 | £28,500 |
| 1891 | Hupeh | 428 | T3Cy. | 240 | 1300 | 118 | £8,525 | £33,750 |
| 1891 | Bramham | 389 | T3Cy. | 160 | 1000 | 94 | £5,350 | £22,500 |
| 1891 | Jessie | 425 | T3Cy. | 190 | 1200 | 115 | £6,400 | £25,250 |
| 1891 | Ruabon | 427 | T3Cy. | 160 | 1000 | 117 | £5,900 | £22,900 |
| 1891 | Harold | 411 | T3Cy. | 168 | 1000 | 100 | £5,250 | £20,500 |
| 1891 | Castleton | 421 | T3Cy. | 190 | 1200 | 111 | £6,650 | £25,250 |
| 1891 | Inchbarra / Telesfora | 419 | T3Cy. | 500 | 2000 | 109 | £12,000 | £46,750 |
| 1891 | Saint Andrews | 423 | T3Cy. | 250 | 1300 | 113 | £8,500 | £31,400 |
| 1891 | Westow | 424 | T3Cy. | 200 | 1200 | 114 | £6,750 | £25,850 |
| 1891 | Mab | 422 | T3Cy. | 220 | 1200 | 112 | £7,750 | £30,325 |
| 1891 | Rhio | 418 | T3Cy. | 120 | 800 | 108 | £4,350 | £16,500 |
| 1891 | Blenheim | 408 | T3Cy. | 215 | 1205 | 96 | £7,000 | £26,400 |
| 1891 | Lesbury | 413 | T3Cy. | 240 | 1300 | 99 | £7,700 | n.k. |
| 1891 | Lincolnshire | 410 | T3Cy. | 240 | 1300 | 98 | £8,550 | £30.235 |
| 1891 | Rothesay | 414 | T3Cy. | 160 | 1000 | 102 | £5,475 | £21,750 |
| 1891 | General Boyd | 415 | C2Cy. | 217 | 900 | 103 | £4,400 | £16,800 |
| 1891 | Holmlea | 417 | T3Cy. | 150 | 900 | 107 | £5,050 | £20,000 |
| 1891 | Heighington | 405 | T3Cy. | 239 | 1300 | 93 | £7,750 | £30,750 |
| 1891 | Adelphi Chrissoveloni | 416 | T3Cy. | 200 | 1250 | 104 | £6,900 | £25,900 |
| 1891 | Hardanger | 420 | T3Cy. | 215 | 1250 | 110 | £6,900 | £26,400 |
| 1891 | Shantung | 429 | T3Cy. | 240 | 1300 | 119 | £8,525 | £33,750 |
| 1891 | Elmete | 412 | T3Cy. | 160 | 1000 | 101 | £5,350 | £22,500 |
| 1891 | Ariadne | 426 | T3Cy. | 160 | 1000 | 116 | £5,800 | £22,200 |
| 1892 | Ramillies | 445 | T3Cy. | 250 | 1550 | 137 | £8,250 | £29,250 |
| 1892 | Melbourne | 435 | T3Cy. | 162 | 900 | 125 | £5,250 | £19,500 |
| 1892 | Thyra | 432 | T3Cy. | 240 | 1500 | 122 | £8,650 | £33,750 |
| 1892 | Mashona | 437 | T3Cy. | 500 | 2000 | 127 | £9,450 | £32,500 |
| 1892 | Nina Mendl | 440 | T3Cy. | 250 | 1300 | 131 | £7,500 | £26,500 |
| 1892 | Aldworth | 455 | T3Cy. | 279 | 1600 | 147 | £8,800 | £28,500 |
| 1892 | Conch | 448 | T3Cy. | 324 | 2000 | 140 | £10,250 | £47,000 |
| 1892 | Masonic | 433 | T3Cy. | 220 | 1800 | 123 | £7,500 | £24,750 |
| 1892 | Murex | 442 | T3Cy. | 324 | 2000 | 130 | £10,250 | £47,000 |
| 1892 | Escholbrook | 446 | T3Cy. | 207 | 1200 | 135 | £6,250 | £23,400 |
| 1892 | Argyll | 439 | T3Cy. | 283 | 1300 | 129 | £9,587 | £34,000 |
| 1892 | Blagdon | 454 | T3Cy. | 140 | 1000 | 146 | £5,650 | £21,750 |
| 1892 | Quantock/Florence Pile | 441 | T3Cy. | 279 | 1600 | 134 | £8,600 | £33,500 |
| 1892 | Manica | 438 | T3Cy. | 500 | 2000 | 128 | £9,450 | £32,500 |
| 1892 | Spheroid | 430 | T3Cy. | 220 | 1300 | 120 | £8,000 | n.k. |
| 1892 | James Tucker | 458 | T3Cy. | 220 | 1300 | 151 | £7,450 | £27,000 |
| 1892 | Arapahoe / Inchmaree | 444 | T3Cy. | 500 | 2600 | 133 | £12,000 | £44,500 |
| 1892 | Buckminster | 453 | T3Cy. | 175 | 1000 | 145 | £5,550 | £21,750 |
| 1892 | Mount Stewart | 431 | T3Cy. | 120 | 800 | 121 | £4,500 | £12,350 |
| 1892 | Venus | 436 | T3Cy. | 113 | 700 | 126 | £3,750 | £15,500 |
| 1892 | Alberta / Inchulva | 443 | T3Cy. | 500 | 2250 | 132 | £12,000 | £44,500 |
| 1892 | Milo | 434 | T3Cy. | 156 | 900 | 124 | £5,050 | £19,000 |
| 1892 | Hildawell | 452 | T3Cy. | 224 | 1250 | 144 | £6,900 | £26,250 |
| 1893 | Pacific | 469 | T3Cy. | 224 | 1500 | 163 | £6,950 | £25,000 |

| YEAR | SHIP | No. | TYPE | NHP | IHP | No. | ENG | SHIP COST |
|------|------|-----|------|-----|-----|-----|-----|-----------|
| 1893 | Penarth | 463 | T3Cy. | 290 | 1500 | 155 | £8,200 | £30,300 |
| 1893 | Nador | 460 | T3Cy. | 167 | 1000 | 153 | £5,550 | £21,630 |
| 1893 | Elax | 450 | T3Cy. | 357 | 2250 | 143 | £11,000 | £52,000 |
| 1893 | Baracaldo | 467 | T3Cy. | 127 | 700 | 160 | £3,830 | n.k. |
| 1893 | Adjutant | 461 | T3Cy. | 240 | 1250 | 152 | £7,000 | £26,000 |
| 1893 | Ariadne Alexandra | 466 | T3Cy. | 175 | 1000 | 159 | £5,300 | n.k. |
| 1893 | David Mainland | 468 | T3Cy. | 156 | 900 | 161 | £4,400 | £18,650 |
| 1893 | Bullmouth | 465 | T3Cy. | 357 | 2250 | 157 | £11,000 | £52,000 |
| 1893 | Burma | 456 | T3Cy. | 256 | 1200 | 142 | £8,400 | £30,600 |
| 1893 | Oscar II | 457 | T3Cy. | 220 | 1300 | 149 | £7,700 | £29,950 |
| 1893 | Castanos | 471 | T3Cy. | 258 | 1500 | 167 | £6,700 | £26,950 |
| 1893 | Roumania / Algorteno | 462 | T3Cy. | 239 | 1300 | 154 | £7,700 | £25,750 |
| 1893 | Webster | 459 | T3Cy. | 270 | 1500 | 150 | £8,400 | n.k. |
| 1893 | Clam | 449 | T3Cy. | 299 | 2000 | 141 | £10,250 | £47,000 |
| 1893 | Volute | 451 | T3Cy. | 399 | 2250 | 148 | £11,000 | £52,000 |
| 1894 | Ribston | 472 | T3Cy. | 260 | - | 169 | £6,850 | £29,500 |
| 1894 | Strathord | 482 | T3Cy. | 404 | 1600 | 180 | £10,250 | £39,000 |
| 1894 | Lady Gray | 479 | T3Cy. | 224 | 1200 | 176 | £6,150 | £23,680 |
| 1894 | South Gwalia / Povena | 478 | T3Cy. | 188 | - | 172 | £5,000 | £20,475 |
| 1894 | Garton | 477 | T3Cy. | 239 | - | 174 | £6,650 | £26,000 |
| 1894 | Chatburn | 474 | T3Cy. | 169 | - | 166 | £4,750 | £19,200 |
| 1894 | Coniscliffe/Urquiola | 476 | T3Cy. | 224 | - | 175 | £6,000 | £23,950 |
| 1894 | Strathnairn | 480 | T3Cy. | 404 | - | 171 | £10,250 | £39,000 |
| 1894 | Strathfillan | 486 | T3Cy. | 404 | 1600 | 181 | £10,250 | £39,000 |
| 1894 | Emmanuel / Graphic | 485 | T3Cy. | 239 | - | 183 | £6,600 | £25,500 |
| 1894 | Rounton | 473 | T3Cy. | 239 | - | 173 | £6,450 | £24,500 |
| 1894 | Strathness / Buceros | 475 | T3Cy. | 404 | - | 170 | £10,250 | £39,000 |
| 1894 | Severus | 483 | T3Cy. | 295 | 1200 | 179 | £7,200 | £28,775 |
| 1894 | Bayvoe / Wenvoe | 481 | T3Cy. | 258 | 1200 | 177 | £6,900 | £27,450 |
| 1894 | Bainbridge | 484 | T3Cy. | 140 | - | 182 | £4,550 | £19,000 |
| 1895 | Penarth | 508 | T3Cy. | 266 | 1200 | 508 | £7,600 | £28,250 |
| 1895 | Holgate | 511 | T3Cy. | 244 | 1100 | 511 | £6,500 | £25,000 |
| 1895 | Middleton | 496 | T3Cy. | 239 | 1100 | 195 | £7,000 | £26,000 |
| 1895 | Pectan | 498 | T3Cy. | 398 | 1700 | 197 | £12,000 | £60,500 |
| 1895 | Baluchistan | 510 | T3Cy. | 224 | 1000 | 510 | £5,850 | £22,850 |
| 1895 | Haslingden | 490 | T3Cy. | 169 | 750 | 187 | £4,850 | £19,450 |
| 1895 | Parklands / Ameland | 494 | T3Cy. | 239 | 1100 | 193 | £7,000 | £26,600 |
| 1895 | Majestic | 500 | T3Cy. | 239 | 1100 | 199 | £6,600 | £25,500 |
| 1895 | Martin | 487 | T3Cy. | 156 | 700 | 184 | £4,560 | £19,000 |
| 1895 | Lady Olivia/Kirkstall | 505 | T3Cy. | 156 | 700 | 505 | £4,500 | £18,350 |
| 1895 | Telena | 499 | T3Cy. | 398 | 1700 | 198 | £12,000 | £60,500 |
| 1895 | Mathilda | 497 | T3Cy. | 260 | 1200 | 196 | £7,400 | £31,000 |
| 1895 | Lesreaulx | 488 | T3Cy. | 258 | 1200 | 185 | £7,200 | £28,500 |
| 1895 | Argo | 501 | T3Cy. | 271 | 1200 | 501 | £7,200 | £27,750 |
| 1895 | Elfie | 495 | T3Cy. | 156 | 700 | 194 | £4,800 | £19,750 |
| 1895 | Bertholey | 509 | T3Cy. | 223 | 1000 | 509 | £6,600 | £23,750 |
| 1895 | Romsdalen | 493 | T3Cy. | 224 | 1000 | 192 | £6,300 | £24,250 |
| 1895 | Clermiston / Rocio | 491 | T3Cy. | 127 | 600 | 189 | £4,250 | £15,750 |
| 1895 | Rossall | 492 | T3Cy. | 225 | 1100 | 191 | £6,700 | £26,100 |
| 1895 | Maling | 489 | T3Cy. | 241 | 1200 | 186 | £7,200 | n.k. |
| 1895 | Marie Elsie | 504 | T3Cy. | 247 | 1100 | 504 | £6,750 | £26,000 |
| 1895 | Saint Ronald | 503 | T3Cy. | 218 | 1200 | 503 | £7,600 | £28,640 |
| 1895 | Firby | 506 | T3Cy. | 224 | 1000 | 506 | £5,900 | n.k. |
| 1895 | Nanette | 507 | T3Cy. | 224 | 1000 | 507 | £5,900 | £22,450 |

| YEAR | SHIP | No. | TYPE | NHP | IHP | No. | ENG | SHIP COST |
|------|------|-----|------|-----|-----|-----|-----|-----------|
| 1895 | Aries | 502 | T3Cy. | 271 | 1200 | 502 | £7,200 | £27,750 |
| 1896 | Cambrian / Bostonian | 524 | T3Cy. | 660 | 4000 | 524 | £11,000 | £79,500 |
| 1896 | Jupiter | 519 | T3Cy. | 148 | 900 | 519 | £4,500 | £19,200 |
| 1896 | Sigurd | 516 | T3Cy. | 198 | 1100 | 516 | £5,300 | £21,300 |
| 1896 | Dalegarth | 527 | T3Cy. | 238 | 1200 | 527 | £6,250 | £19,285 |
| 1896 | Margareta / Inchmona | 512 | Quad. | 326 | 2200 | 512 | £7,250 | £29,350 |
| 1896 | Mars | 523 | T3Cy. | 148 | 800 | 523 | £4,500 | £19,500 |
| 1896 | Balderton | 522 | T3Cy. | 244 | 1300 | 522 | £6,400 | £25,000 |
| 1896 | Ebani / Loong Sang | 515 | T3Cy. | 245 | 1200 | 515 | £6,750 | £23,350 |
| 1896 | Simonside | 517 | T3Cy. | 266 | 1500 | 517 | £7,600 | £28,750" |
| 1896 | Atlantic/Brattingsborg | 521 | T3Cy. | 271 | 1300 | 521 | £7,500 | £28,800 |
| 1896 | Laristan | 526 | T3Cy. | 218 | 1200 | 526 | £5,550 | £22,750 |
| 1896 | Greylands / Ed.Gustave | 514 | T3Cy. | 244 | 1300 | 514 | £6,450 | £25,500 |
| 1896 | Alette | 520 | T3Cy. | 279 | 1550 | 520 | £7,292 | £31,500 |
| 1896 | Gallia | 528 | T3Cy. | 188 | 1000 | 528 | £5,000 | £21,250 |
| 1896 | Ragnar | 518 | T3Cy. | 198 | 1000 | 518 | £5,300 | £21,300 |
| 1896 | Jomsborg | 525 | T3Cy. | 188 | 1000 | 525 | £5,000 | £21,000 |
| 1896 | Taisho Maru / Valhalla | 513 | T3Cy. | 225 | 1250 | 513 | £6,000 | £24,959 |
| 1897 | Afghanistan | 531 | T3Cy. | 240 | 1300 | 531 | £6,550 | £25,500 |
| 1897 | Arlington | 537 | T3Cy. | 260 | 1500 | 537 | £7,700 | n.k. |
| 1897 | Helga | 534 | T3Cy. | 127 | 800 | 534 | £4,250 | £16,250 |
| 1897 | Eveline | 536 | T3Cy. | 244 | 1300 | 536 | £6,650 | £25,950 |
| 1897 | Olaf | 530 | T3Cy. | 198 | 1100 | 530 | £5,300 | £21,400 |
| 1897 | Martha / Marselisborg | 535 | T3Cy. | 127 | 800 | 535 | £4,250 | £16,250 |
| 1897 | Koordistan | 548 | T3Cy. | 239 | 1300 | 548 | £7,625 | £28,250 |
| 1897 | Sturton | 539 | T3Cy. | 220 | 1200 | 539 | £5,750 | £23,200 |
| 1897 | Vlug | 529 | T3Cy. | 127 | 800 | 529 | £4,150 | £16,250 |
| 1897 | Atlas | 541 | T3Cy. | 260 | 1500 | 541 | £7,550 | £30,000 |
| 1897 | Alpha | 545 | T3Cy. | 165 | 900 | 545 | £4,900 | £20,750 |
| 1897 | Olivemoor | 542 | T3Cy. | 260 | 1500 | 542 | £7,450 | £29,600 |
| 1897 | Britannic / Aldersgate | 532 | T3Cy. | 281 | 1500 | 532 | £7,600 | £29,250 |
| 1897 | Sceptre | 540 | T3Cy. | 244 | 1300 | 540 | £6,650 | £25,750 |
| 1897 | Pallas | 543 | T3Cy. | 156 | 900 | 543 | £4,800 | £20,250 |
| 1897 | Harlingen/Ethelbrytha | 547 | T3Cy. | 295 | 1700 | 547 | £8,300 | £30,700 |
| 1897 | Saint Helen | 544 | T3Cy. | 244 | 1200 | 544 | £6,800 | £27,500 |
| 1897 | Pendennis | 533 | T3Cy. | 218 | 1200 | 533 | £5,600 | £23,200 |
| 1897 | Ambassador | 538 | T3Cy. | 242 | 1300 | 538 | £6,650 | £26,500 |
| 1897 | Cresyl | 546 | T3Cy. | 227 | 1250 | 546 | £6,600 | £25,450 |
| 1898 | Emanuel | 551 | T3Cy. | 150 | 900 | 551 | £5,000 | £20,250 |
| 1898 | Cardiff | 554 | T3Cy. | 255 | 1300 | 554 | £7,300 | £28,900 |
| 1898 | Sanna | 550 | T3Cy. | 292 | 1500 | 550 | £8,500 | £34,000 |
| 1898 | Povena | 553 | T3Cy. | 206 | 1200 | 553 | £6,150 | £22,500 |
| 1898 | Goolistan | 549 | T3Cy. | 240 | 1300 | 549 | £7,625 | £28,250 |
| 1898 | Algorta | 552 | T3Cy. | 208 | 1200 | 552 | £6,150 | £22,500 |
| 1898 | Turkistan | 566 | T3Cy. | 460 | 2550 | 566 | £12,600 | £37,500 |
| 1899 | Helsingborg | 600 | T3Cy. | 221 | 1250 | 600 | £7,500 | £30,000 |
| 1899 | Inchkeith | 583 | Quad. | 310 | 2000 | 583 | £12,500 | £41,500 |
| 1899 | Nubia | 599 | T3Cy. | 310 | 2000 | 599 | £10,750 | £43,000 |
| 1899 | Sandsend | 598 | T3Cy. | 321 | 2000 | 598 | £10,500 | £41,500 |
| 1900 | Inchmarlo / Rhenania | 616 | Quad. | 299 | 2000 | 616 | £14,200 | £50,000 |
| 1900 | Toronto | 603 | 2T3Cy | 660 | 5600 | 603 | £24,500 | £93,960 |
| 1900 | Inchdune | 614 | Quad. | 299 | 2000 | 614 | £14,200 | £50,000 |
| 1900 | Nassovia | 623 | Quad. | 274 | 2000 | 623 | £16,750 | £56,250 |
| 1901 | Atheniana | 650 | T3Cy. | 225 | 1250 | 650 | £7,700 | £27,500 |

| YEAR | SHIP | No. | TYPE | NHP | IHP | No. | ENG | SHIP COST |
|------|------|-----|------|-----|-----|-----|------|-----------|
| 1901 | Marie Z. Michalinos | 649 | T3Cy. | 300 | 1700 | 649 | £10,405 | £41,000 |
| 1901 | Holmeside | 643 | T3Cy. | 322 | 2000 | 643 | £10,880 | £51,500 |
| 1912 | Arabistan / Chinwarh | 802 | T3Cy. | 603 | 3710 | 802 | £16,750 | £57,500 |
| 1912 | Cyrena | 818 | T3Cy. | 270 | 1460 | 818 | £10,350 | £35,000 |
| 1912 | Penolver | 806 | T3Cy. | 336 | 1800 | 806 | £9,200 | £37,500 |
| 1913 | Ubier | 838 | T3Cy. | 288 | 1590 | 838 | £9,000 | £33,750 |
| 1914 | Rosalie | 850 | T3Cy. | 388 | 1734 | 850 | £11,200 | £46,500 |

# APPENDIX 'C'

List of Central Marine Engine Works material held by
Hartlepool Museum Service.

| 1. | | "Anchor Fast Anchor" collected magazines/passim. |
|---|---|---|
| 2. | 69'79 | Company Correspondence Books. |
| 3. | 81'82'2 | Enamelled face plate for ship's telegraph (French). |
| 4. | T1715 | Model of boiler. |
| 5. | T1716 | Certificate for first place in C.M.E.W.'s Apprenticeship Advancement Scheme Award to Thos. L. Rowlands 1928. |

## Photographs Box 25

| 7. | 6'78'1 | Interior of works view of large boiler being built. |
|---|---|---|
| 8. | 34'86 (3937) | Twin Gray-Polar |
| 9. | 34'86 (4927) | View of the C.M.E.W. Yard taken from No. 8 warehouse, Middleton Road. |
| 10. | 2974 | Model of Marine High Pressure Boiler. |
| 11. | 2982-7 2989 | Assorted photographs of C.M.E.W. (external views). |
| 12. | 1774 1777 | First shows Modern Welding Techniques in 1956 in the boiler shop, second shows the Erecting Shop C.M.E.W. |
| 13. | 2610 | View of crane with boiler for unknown ship. |
| 14. | 2611-13 | 3 stills from a film showing workmen receiving their bait-boxes from children. |
| 15. | 4847- | C.M.E.W. 1920's. |
| 16. | 1694-5 | 1890's Boilers. |
| 17. | 1765-73 | 1890's Assorted. |
| 18. | 1096- 1701 | Doxford No. 298 – 6 views. |
| 19. | 3934 | Babcock Wilcox. |

## EPHEMERA, ROBERT WOOD COLL.
Box 16 – Acc. No. 63'77

| 20. | A'2426 | Specification for Patent Quadruple to Crank Engines. |
|---|---|---|
| 21. | A'2422 | Notice about Summer Time working. |
| 22. | | Funeral Notice for Thomas Mudd and other material. |

## Ephemera (MSS/6/E2)

| 23. | 69'79'1' & 2 | Apprentice Advancement Scheme 1902 and Fire Brigade Rules & Regulations both MS/6/E2. |
|---|---|---|
| 24. | 174'71'2 | Specification of a Triple Engine. |
| 25. | 5'78'3 | Catalogue of Gray's Sale (Shipyard, etc.) 1963. |
| 26. | T140 | Instructions, etc. concerning C.M.E.W. Drop valve Gear (Inside Spring Type). |
| 27. | T3614 | Booklet with details about various items produced by the firm, (e.g. Patent Oil Fuel Separators). |

# INDEX

# INDEX Continued

# INDEX Continued

Fitting boilers to m.v. "Castledore" 1957.

Doxford pistons, boring mills (auxiliary shop, C.M.E.W.)

# FAST ANCHOR

VOL. 2    JANUARY, 1959    No. 8

FAST ANCHOR